A nort

A comprehensive revi
dying in the North W

I.

Other books by the same author

Cotton Everywhere
Thanatology of the Child
A Thanatology of War

A northern thanatology

A comprehensive review of illness, death and dying in the North West of England from the 1500s to the present time

by

Christine Kenny

with contributions from
Bill Flynn and Joan Miller

Quay Books Division, Mark Allen Publishing Group
Jesses Farm, Snow Hill, Dinton, Wiltshire, SP3 5HN

British Library Cataloguing-in-Publication Data
A catalogue record is available for this book

© Christine Kenny 1998
ISBN 1 85642 096 5

Printed in the UK by Cromwell Press, Trowbridge, Wiltshire

Contents

Acknowledgements

Acknowledgements are difficult because those of us who write receive so much support from various sources that there is always the worry that someone might be omitted. I also have to give acknowledgements not only for myself, but also on behalf of Bill Flynn and my mother, Joan Miller, who made contributions to this book.

To begin with I would like to thank all of those who took part in the study. Without their contributions, the book could not have been written. Thanks also to the staff of Bolton Central Library Local History section — you were all wonderful and patient in helping me research archive material for this series. Thanks to my family and especially my children for putting up with all the hours I spent on this book and for encouraging me every inch of the way. Thanks also to my colleagues at South Bank University, in particular Keith Cooper, Tony Leiba and Pittu Laungani, and to Len Barton of the University of Sheffield and Colin Barnes of the University of Leeds. Valery Marston also deserves a special thanks for all her encouragement, patience and support.

Finally, a special, special thanks to my Dad and Mike Dobbie of South Bank University for sorting out my PC nightmares.

Christine Kenny

Introduction

Thanatology is the term used to describe a multidisciplinary approach to the study of death, dying and bereavement. This book is Volume 1 of a Thanatology of Lancashire in the North West of England. It covers the period from the 1500s to the present but excludes the war years. Death takes on different meanings during a war and we felt unable to do justice to the topic in a single text.

Volume 2, 'A thanatology of war', explores death, dying and bereavement during the two wars. Volume 3, 'A thanatology of the child' is more directly applied than its predecessors and has been written for parents and professional people who work with children and young people. All three volumes are aimed at a wide readership and we hope that both academics and non-academics will find something of interest. Reading about any community issue broadens our minds and helps us to understand ourselves and our communities a little better. Many historians believe the greatest value of historical research is that it can lead to increased understanding of self (Burns and Grove, 1987). This is particularly relevant when considering death and dying. Our mortality is the one commonalty we all share. Thoughts about death influence ideas and thoughts about life.

How the series evolved

Initially, the series began with the work of Christine Kenny and her research into northern women's experiences of working in the textile industry. From this research she wrote a semi-autobiographic book called 'Cotton Everywhere'. To gather data for the book, Christine interviewed 14 older Bolton women aged between 55 and 90 years of age. So much data was collected that it became impossible to include all the issues, which arose in the transcripts, in one book. Health, illness, death and dying were some of the themes not included.

However, it was not Christine's intention to ignore these themes. Instead she decided to build on them by conducting further research. She also felt that the issues to be explored might be presented in more interesting ways if she was to develop a partnership with other academics. This began with Bill Flynn and Liz Foster, both lecturers from Bolton Community Education Service and Bolton Institute. It was appropriate to link up with lecturers from Bolton Education Services because of their involvement in the area. The rationale underpinning the establishment of Bolton Education Service is linked directly to the history of the borough (which includes the outlying townships of Farnworth, Westhoughton, etc) and the town's rise and fall in terms of the cotton-related industries. These fluctuations in the economy are typical of many other Lancashire towns and are well-documented in economic history textbooks. What is not so well-documented are the experiences of people whose lives were affected by these fluctuations and who must cope with the legacy of economic decline. During the nineteenth century, Bolton and the surrounding townships were boom areas in relation to the cotton industry. By the 1870s service industries, such as shops and banks, were on the rise as part of a maturing economy. But so was competition from newly established industrial economies such as Germany and the USA.

By the 1920s and 1930s employment in the traditional industries became sporadic and despite post-war government attempts to protect them, manufacturing and coal mining declined rapidly. At the time of writing there are only two mills left in Bolton and no pits, and many related industries have closed. There has been a substantial rise in service industries, but not enough to compensate for the decline in manufacturing. The result is high levels of unemployment and derelict mills and townships. Some areas have been taken over by 'cut price' stores: town centres like Farnworth are dominated by cheap 'seconds' stores, charity shops, second-hand markets and so on. The old housing stock, built originally to house the mill workers, are now occupied by immigrants and their families (encouraged to come to the area during the full employment era of the 1950s), and those who cannot afford to move out.[1]

This continuing deterioration prompted the Faculty of the old Bolton College to develop a partnership with communities suffering from the worst effects of the economic decline. Community Education targeted the areas highest in the 'league table' of deprivation, in the belief that education (in its broadest sense) is valuable and, if barriers could be broken down, people who had been disadvantaged by the institutional education 'system' would respond. It was also believed that, if given a wide range of opportunities, the pattern of low income areas having high rates of low educational achievement could be reversed.

Achieving this is a long and difficult process. Going into an area, perhaps for the first time, trying to set up groups with preconceived ideas about education; maintaining a distinction between community education and the more formal adult education, is not easy. Nor is it easy to quantify outcomes. Planting the seeds of intrinsically motivated learning is difficult but concrete results are attainable. This is where informal versus formal education unites as some of the students from Community Education move on to complete degrees, usually at Bolton Institute.

Bolton Institute and Community Education have the same commitment to equal opportunities. Collaborative work between the two establishments has increased in recent years. Lecturers from Community Education make contributions to courses at the Institute, particularly to the Community Studies pathway of the Combined Honours framework. Of course not everyone who uses the Community Education services wishes to go on to Higher Education. But, due to the increased co-operation between the colleges, greater opportunities for this now exist. Linking up with South Bank University opens up the potential for educational establishments, with a strong commitment to equal opportunities, to learn from each other. It is hoped that the publication of this series will also help to open up such

---

1   The writers acknowledge that not everyone wants to move out of
     the areas discussed.

potential, if only in a very modest way. Contributions have been made by some of the author's new colleagues at South Bank. Founded as a charity in the 1800s, South Bank University (formally Borough Polytechnic) is one of the largest London universities. The university has an unparalleled international, social gender and ethnic mix and a firm commitment to the principles of equal opportunities.

Conducting such collaborative work has been extremely difficult but well worth the effort. 'Cotton Everywhere' had a personal element underpinning it which provided a specific and individual perspective to part of Bolton's history. This personal element gave the book a quality which would have been unattainable in a collaborative publication. 'Cotton Everywhere' presented one way of viewing the past but it did not, of course, present the only way. The advantage of a collaborative piece of work is that each of the authors has been able to add insights and perspectives from their own intellectual resources. This allows a broader, multidisciplinary approach which could not have been achieved by any one individual. Academics from all the disciplines have an interest in death and dying. The value of a multidisciplinary approach has been increasingly recognised as various professional groups draw on theory to improve their practice.

Criticisms of social science research

This thanatology series has a more academic approach than 'Cotton Everywhere'. We hope, however, that the theoretical approaches we have taken do not detract from the wide readership we hope to attract. Academic theory is becoming increasingly applied to practical settings, although this has not always been the case[2]. Social science has come under

---

2   Two of the many changes in education that may have led to such critiques and subsequent changes, include: the move from an elite system of education to mass education and the change in many professions from an apprentice type of training to that of an education which confers professional qualifications, ie. a university degree, and academic status.

considerable criticism in the past for being too abstract and seemingly irrelevant to everyday life. The objectivity and political neutrality claimed by many social science researchers has also been questioned. Becker was one of the first to challenge this claim in his 1967 paper 'Whose side are we on'. More recent writers, such as Sieber (1992), have argued that much social science research can be unhelpful and even, at times, extremely unethical. Other workers show that the conclusions drawn by some researchers have been positively damaging to the people they have studied (Oliver, 1991; Finch, 1993). Feminists like other academics have been criticised for presenting their work in a style, very difficult to understand, which excludes the very people (many women) they claim to be trying to empower (Anderson, 1992; Palmer, 1993). Western middle-class feminists have also been criticised for failing to address the concerns of black women, disabled and working-class women (De Bois and Ruiz, 1990).

These criticisms have caused some writers to argue that social scientists should try to conduct research **with** rather than **on** people (Oakley, 1991; Miles, 1993). The idea is that people who participate in research should benefit by it in some way. How participants benefit from research varies. Christine Kenny used her initial interviews to write 'Cotton Everywhere' which was a 'popular' book, accessible to a very wide-reading audience. The book aimed to appeal to older people who remembered the mills and to younger people who had no experience of them. Audio taped copies were also made available for people with sight problems. All of the 14 women who took part in the study received free complementary copies. Her aim was to produce a local history which was interesting, informative, easy to read and fairly cheap to buy. Although we have drawn on theory to produce 'A thanatology of the north', our aims are very similar. Some academics have pointed out that taking part in research can be enjoyable and beneficial (Hutchinson *et al*, 1994). Participation in interviews can help to make people feel valued because it validates their experience (Coles, 1989; Frisby and Tucker, 1993). Oral history in particular provides a voice for those who have been excluded from history (Doyle *et al*, 1973). Researchers can learn as much about themselves from their work as they do about those they study. Conducting research, therefore, can facilitate personal growth and development in the researcher (Frisch, 1990). Indeed, research can be a partnership between the researcher and those who participate. This Stuart (1993) discovered when the women she interviewed asked at the conclusion 'How was it for you Mary?'

Researching local histories and communities

Drawing his inspiration from Newton, Lumby (1995) argues that 'a community which delights in its history is thereby tickled into life and emboldened to face new ventures'. Lancashire has a very rich history. Old Lancashire was a vast area scanning an excess of a million acres. It had an extreme length of 85 miles and a breadth of 46 miles, laying between Westmorland, Cumberland, Yorkshire, Cheshire and the Irish Sea (Johnson, 1996). Lancashire was very sparsely populated until the Industrial Revolution in the nineteenth century, following which the population soared. The history of Lancashire both prior to and following the industrial revolution is fascinating. In this book we draw on the history of Lancashire to construct our thanatology of the north.

In the 1950s, local history and community studies were relatively new areas of study in education (Warren, 1955). Since this time interest in both subjects has expanded. At the time of writing they could be referred to with considerable confidence as 'boom areas' in education. Other related fields include urban and cultural studies, women's studies, black studies and health studies — to name but a few. These subject areas adopt an eclectic approach, drawing on the more traditional disciplines such as psychology and sociology (Gough, 1989). There is a commitment to making theory more applied (McKeon, 1977) and in adopting a 'real world' approach to research.[3]

These 'real world' approaches can, however, be confusing and just as saturated with academic jargon as the more traditional approaches they are supposed to challenge.

---

3   This basically means looking at the real world or getting outside of the 'Ivory Tower'.

Approaches favoured within this new model include ethnography, grounded theory, story telling, narrative analysis, action research and many more. What can be so confusing (even to academics) is the high level of similarity between them all (Bonet, 1994). The authors of this book found it very difficult as a matter of fact, to decide what it is that we are doing. Is this series an ethnography or a social history of death and dying? For this series we decided that grounded theory would provide the most accurate definition. However, at the risk of appearing contradictory, the work is not utterly and completely what one might describe as grounded theory. Grounded theory is an exploratory approach in which the theory is meant to evolve from the data. In volume one this immediately presents problems. This is a descriptive study with very little theoretical discussion. It does, however, form the basis of the theoretical discussions developed in volumes two and three. There are also parts of the research that might be described as phenomenology and possibly hermeneutics. The study then adopts a combined approach. Conway (1996) argues that a combined approach can help to compensate for the weaknesses of each.

This study necessitated the adoption of a combined approach because of its breadth. The history constructed from the 1500s to the mid twentieth century has drawn on archive material and secondary sources. Data collected to construct the history from the 1930s to the present time, includes interview and survey material as well as archive material. The interviews have been quite interactive because the researcher who conducted them knows most of the people who took part in the study (Kenny and Wibberley, 1994). For those who wish to conduct their own research into community issues, sources of data include library sources, minutes from meetings, official reports, statistics and census reports. More personal sources can include photographs, letters, diaries and school reports (Parker, 1944). In the North in recent years, there has been a proliferation of books written by local authors. Though produced as 'popular' texts many of these are very well written and excellent sources of secondary reading. For example, for this book the writers have drawn on a number of local books, such as Lumby's book on the Lancashire Witches and Dale's book on the growth of religion in Bolton.[4] These, and indeed all of the local books we have used as our secondary sources, are well written and academically sound. Given the expense of books today and shrinking student grants, we feel that students should be encouraged to use these books for their studies as well as the texts produced by academic publishers. This would have the double benefit of promoting and encouraging local writers while at the same time saving students money. Boltonians are very fortunate to have an excellent local history section in the town's Central Library. The most valuable sources of information in any community are of course its people. Much of the data collected for this series have been based on interviews conducted with older people — in other words, oral history.

Critics of oral history frequently contrast this approach with the greater reliability of documentary evidence, but these sources often have their own biases and distortions (Lummis, 1987). Issues that have been omitted from official documents can be of real interest to future generations. Until very recently most historians, even local historians, tended to belong to the governing and upper social classes and considered wider social and political issues to be more important than ordinary events effecting ordinary people (Thompson, 1978). Sometimes historical reports are far from accurate or objective and can blatantly justify violence and oppression inflicted on marginal groups by the more dominant members of a society (Parker, 1991). Many documents which contain interesting insights into history, such as minutes of small societies, personal letters and the papers of small businesses, have been destroyed or lost because those who kept such records did not consider them to be of any importance. Even when the keeping of official records of marriages, births and deaths, for example, became more efficient, there was still much which had been lost (Thompson, *op cit*). Finally, there is no reason to assume that oral history should be kept separate from more conservative sources, the two can be used together (Goodman, 1994).

4   Each of these books are excellent value for money and can be purchased for less than £10.

Oral history and memory

Critics of oral history also consider autobiographic memory a problem because people forget, distort events in their minds or simply tell lies. Research does suggest that autobiographic memory differs in many ways from other classes of knowledge, such as conceptual and factual knowledge. Autobiographic memories have a direct and strong self-reference, contain sensory and perceptual knowledge related to the encoding environment and constitute personal interpretation of events rather than literal accounts (Conway, 1990a). But it is the nature of autobiographic memory which makes it so valuable (John, 1992). Lummis (1987) further argues that people are likely to report events more accurately many years after because they often consider that the consequences of 'telling' are less risky. Stanley (1994) argues that:

> *'Memory has its limits; but let us not forget that so too do all other ways of researching social life, in the present as well as the past. We should also not forget that memory has an enormous strength, one which gives it an enormous advantage over other research approaches, because only memory based on direct experience has the power to make readers feel that they can almost smell the same smells, almost hear the same sounds, almost feel the same feelings.'*

Bolton is lucky to have some local history groups who collect reminiscence in circulars, such as 'The Little Piecer', produced by the Halliwell Local History Society. Another way of putting history into a community is to encourage local people to write about their lives. Sometimes the aim of such publishing is encompassed within an educational framework. One such example is the magazines distributed by the Bolton Community Education group. The rationale behind the project was to reach out to as many people in the community as possible and, at the same time, increase their level of pride and self-confidence. The background to the development of this style of magazine developed by the project begins in 1986/87. The start of outreach work in the Deane, Derby and Doubhill areas of Bolton, coincided with an adult writing development project in the borough. The two became united after the outreach worker had set up a local history group in response to local interest. During group discussions, an older man continuously spoke of his experiences of Bolton. Prompted by samples from the writing project, he was invited to write his memories down. His story was then typed up and put into print. Other stories were added by the outreach worker visiting people and taking notes from people contacted in the area through the group. Members of the group taped, edited, printed, collated and distributed the first magazine.

The magazine was extremely successful, perhaps because it was free (now 50p) but more likely for deeper reasons. For example, during one of the meetings of the local history group it was found that the bulk of the local history at that time worked on the 'great men' theme. Very little dealt with ordinary working people, the good and bad in their lives, the way they lived, worked and played. Nor was there much history about the local streets and houses that were rapidly disappearing. The magazine started to redress this imbalance. Moreover, the stories were written as people told them.

There were many mistakes, but this was seen as 'human', as were the stories. People treasured them, cried over them, and sent them to all parts of the world. They were placed in schools and children used them for history projects. The older man discussed above, became a local celebrity. His picture appeared in the local paper and requests came from various sources for him to talk to groups of children and young people. This success was maintained through four further issues of the magazine.

This prompted the outreach worker to produce further issues and to expand by working with other groups in other areas as he moved around the borough. All were based on the same formula of local peoples' stories that could be written by them or told to the worker. There were pictures, and maps to illustrate them and each issue was placed in libraries throughout the borough so that people could borrow copies. So far there have been fifteen magazines in this style, including four — specifically relating to Asian and West Indian stories. At the time of writing, the latest four issues have been based on Farnworth.

With many reprints these magazines are certainly popular. They give an outreach worker access to local people and help to provide an understanding of an area. But do they have a wider value in terms of community development and education? This question is especially relevant when we consider that it is the writing that is important. It is not about developing people's writing skills, although for some it may have been, but on recording the stories of life and experiences. Yet this could be classed as reminiscence work. Again we go back to the problem of definition and, as an academic exercise, the discussion can be very interesting. But, for the purpose of this book, we leave the question open for readers to ponder on while we continue with our history. However, before we embark on the main body of the book, we need to introduce the reader very generally to the field of Thanatology.

What is thanatology?

Thanatology is the name given to the multidisciplinary study of death, dying and bereavement. Perhaps because the reality of our individual mortality is so central to our experience, people have always had an interest in death and dying but for many different reasons. We all have our own ideas about the meaning of life, death and dying. But in academic life people try to understand death from wider, more objective theoretical perspectives. This does not mean that what academics have to say about death is only of interest and relevance to other academics. The psychologist, Kurt Lewin, argued that there is nothing as practical as a good theory. By this Lewin meant that much of the research and other work that academics do has useful, practical implications for almost everyone.[5]

In the area of death and dying, academics from all the disciplines have made valuable contributions to our understanding and much of this has had practical applications. Raphael (1984) writes that 'bereavement is the reaction to the loss of a close relationship and grief is the emotional response to loss, the complex amalgam of painful

5   People often refer to the world outside academia as 'the real world'.

effects including sadness, anger, helplessness, guilt and despair.' How these feelings are experienced and expressed, depends on multifactorial issues. Anthropologists and historians, for example, have demonstrated that almost all human societies have, and have had, religious practices and rituals and emotional responses to bereavement. However, these responses and rituals vary considerably across time and culture. Work by comparative psychologists who study animal behaviour has shown us that some species, such as primates, demonstrate similar emotional responses to the loss of an attachment figure to that observed in human beings. Thus, it appears that while some behaviours in response to loss are hereditary, others are shaped by social and cultural influences (addressed in volumes two and three).

Sociologists, health practitioners, economists and political theorists have shown that death and dying are economic and political issues. The longevity that each individual enjoys and the type of death that each is likely to encounter is shaped by determents such as sex, race and social class. Some countries of the world still employ the use of capital punishment as the penalty for certain offences. However, whether or not an individual is sentenced to death once again depends not only on the crime committed, but on the offender's ethnic identity, social class and gender (Kearl, 1995).

This book traces a history of death rituals in order to explore how social, religious and cultural influences shape the practical and ritualistic aspects of death and dying. It is, therefore, appropriate to call our history a thanatology because we are taking a multidisciplinary approach to develop a holistic understanding of death and dying in the North. In order to develop our discussion, it would be useful first to ask two questions. The first question relates to the title of the book 'A northern thanatology.' Implicit in this title is an assumption that death and dying in Lancashire has always been different, in a variety of ways, from the rest of England, or indeed the world. On what basis are we making this assumption? Is it a valid assumption to make?

On the one hand we can say that we are not absolutely sure. In order to establish if there is a specifically Northern way of death, we would need to do a large scale, comparative study. The authors have neither the money, time or means to conduct a large scale study of this nature. However, we can justify our assumption on the basis of several postulates. The first is that all localities have a specific history which is of interest to people who live in that locality. We have already argued that death and dying are shaped by culture. Within cultures there are subcultures. Lancashire, and in particular Bolton, where the main focus of our study rests, has a culture and local history shaped by influences prior to, during and following the Industrial Revolution.

We can use the case of the Pendle Witches to elaborate this point. Following the Middle Ages, all European communities were consumed by a witch craze. But only Lancashire had a group of women referred to as the Pendle Witches. The Pendle Witches lived in an area which had (has) its own specific characteristics — Lancashire. At the time of the European witch craze, Lancashire was perceived to be something of a sinister 'backward' and deviant area by people in other parts of England. It was very sparsely populated and its people were very resistant to the newly established Church of England.

Many Lancashire people were devout and openly practising Catholics at the time of the Reformation.[6] Despite this, Lancashire only really became a source of grave political concern around the time of the Gunpowder Plot. At this time, many Protestants believed Lancashire to be a resort for Catholic conspirators. Thus, the case of the Pendle Witches was very political having became 'wrapped' in a whole range of issues specific to Lancashire at the time of the Reformation. Thus, the lives, practices,[7] trials and persecution of the Pendle Witches was determined by both European and British concerns.

6   At the time of the Reformation it was illegal to practice as a
     Catholic.
7   We use the word practice here because in the book we explore the
     possibility that the Pendle Witches may have been lay healers. The
     Pendle Witches involvement with death, discussed in *Chapter 3*
     may have had something to do with their healing practice.

The second point to support our assumption, is that other workers have presented evidence to support this view. Researchers who were involved in the Mass Observation Study in the 1930s noted that Bolton funerals were an important characteristic of community life in the town. This observation was supported by a large scale survey conducted by Gorer in the 1960s. Gorer found, unlike many other areas of England at the time, that Northerners reported attendance at funerals as very important to them. Indeed, analysis of Gorer's findings suggest that in the 1960s, people in the North were still celebrating death in the Victorian way.[8]

8   Gorer did not discuss this difference in any depth in his book. It is interesting that Gorer did not consider the difference worthy of further discussion. It was on the basis of the study he conducted for the book that Gorer argued that people no longer observe funeral rituals in the elaborate way that the Victorians had done.

1
Death in a social context

During the late ninteenth century, working-class people developed an ambition to bury their dead 'in style'. As we discuss in *Chapter 9*, this ambition may have been motivated by the desire to have some dignity, at least in death. At the same time, the middle-classes were trying to simplify funerals and reduce the costs. As the towns and cities began to grow, concerns for public health began to effect death rituals. This concern for public health led in turn to the development of more hygienic methods for disposal of the dead. This chapter is concerned with investigating the ways in which social conditions during the Industrial Revolution influenced death rituals, practices and methods of disposing of the dead.

The chapter begins with a discussion of the Industrial Revolution nationally, the growth of towns and cities and related population increase. It then focuses on the Industrial Revolution in the North West of England, the growth of the textile and textile-related industries, and the social conditions in which many Boltonians lived.

The Industrial Revolution

In the mid 1840s, England was still a predominantly rural country. In the years following the 1840s, there was a rapid increase in the establishment of new industries all over the country. Population in the towns and cities rose at an extraordinary rate as immigrants and people from rural areas flooded in to find work (Hibbert, 1977). Initially, improvements and new innovations in industrial technology did not, however, lead to improved standards of living for all. The Industrial Revolution led to the rise of a new and affluent middle-class but pay, working and living conditions for the workers remained very poor and, in some ways, they became even poorer.

Wages were low. Hibbert writes that, in general, factory workers fared better than domestic servants and in some cases, clerical workers. Conditions in the factories were appalling. Houses had been built for the workers, without adequate planning for waste disposal and sanitation. In most industrial towns the poor lived in rows and rows of tiny, back to back cottages packed tightly together. These homes were often damp, poorly ventilated and badly maintained. Several households would have to share public privies and water taps, which were situated in the front streets.

Ash crates for the communal disposal of rubbish were situated in the back streets. Poor sanitation, limited access to water supplies and almost non-existent waste disposal meant that streets were littered with rubbish, decaying waste, dung and excrement. Lack of access to clean water, caused filthy conditions in the home and provision for personal hygiene was very limited. Rivers running through the towns were the source of water for the public taps, but into them drained the filth, waste and excrement from the streets. Victorian writers and commentators reported that the rivers in many towns, had an almost tangible miasma of decay hovering over them. From the 1300s in big cities such as London, officials including the mayor, alderman and common council had been trying hard to improve sanitation and drainage, and to clean up the environment.

Where official bodies were seen to be failing the public, city dwellers sometimes took matters into their own hands. In 1347, for example, at the Assize of Nuisances, it was discovered that two men had been piping their excrement into a neighbour's cellar. The poor design of sanitation and drainage systems were not the only problems. This, poor old Richard the Raker discovered as he plummeted through the rotting planks of his latrine, landing with a big splash into the contents below (Ziegler, 1969).

The Industrial Revolution in the North West of England

As populations in towns and cities increased, there was a corresponding growth in associated problems. In the nineteenth century, observers had noted that the common people who lived in the worst sections of the towns, had an air of lethargy and depression about them (Morley, 1971). This suggests a sense of hopelessness, complicated by ill-health caused by poor nutrition, drinking dirty water, eating contaminated food and living in poverty. A knowledge of history helps us to understand the practices that develop in response to specific situations and which persist long after the rationale for them dies out. In Bolton there had been a custom, religiously observed by older people, of scrubbing the front step every week. This custom survived into the 1970s and could seem quite odd and irritating to younger people who observed it — particularly if pressure was placed on the latter to conform to this custom. But if we consider how dirty the Bolton streets had been in the past, the practice of step scrubbing begins to make sense. After all, no one can change the world, but we can each change our little bit of it. It may be that front step scrubbing developed as a reaction to the filth of the streets. A report published in one of the local papers in 1845[1] stated that:

> *'Our attention has been called to notice the present filthy state of certain parts of Great Bolton, and from inquiries we have made and our own observations we must say that although the principal streets are what might be termed clean, and give that appearance at first sight of what might appear to be a healthy place, yet there are, for those who feel interested and will take the trouble of looking at them, such ill conditioned and nasty places as could not easily be ignored. Stagnant waters, heaps of filth and dunghills abound. The mortality we understand, during the last fortnight has been exceedingly great, although the weather may to some degree have caused more deaths, particularly in old people and children. Owners of property we think, ought to make an attempt to remedy the evil, and if they do not, then it is high time the authorities or public took the matter into their own hands.'*

Despite the problems faced by many working class families, cleanliness and personal hygiene were considered very important. Interviews conducted with the older women who

1   *Bolton Free Press*, December 16th 1845, 2g.

took part in the study suggests that, in the past, the poorer the people, the more importance they placed on maintaining some dignity. This observation has been noted by other workers, who suggest that this may explain why so many working-class people began to place great importance on funerals. The importance of 'keeping up appearances' was also noted by the photographer, Humphrey Spender (1995). When asked why his collection of photographs contained only one domestic interior, Spender commented on the practical difficulties involved, adding:

> *'You might find that a husband and wife, faced with the possibility, might have a conversation beginning on the lines, "Can't let him see that dirty old carpet, must wash the curtains, the dog's absolutely filthy, get him washed, must iron Mary's dress", and so on.'*

The great majority of people, no matter their social situation, may respond in this way to having a stranger, particularly a photographer/researcher, visit their home. The interview material gathered suggests that a concern for cleanliness expressed by older people may have grown from a need to maintain some dignity during times of hardship. Spender's one domestic interior portrays a woman bathing a baby in a zinc tub by the fire, as a man observes. It is an image that is sure to strike strong feelings of nostalgia in many Bolton people. Tin or zinc baths were kept in many households and people would bath in them in front of the fire. Public baths and wash houses, during the early and mid part of this century, also helped to ease some of the problems. But such 'luxuries' were unavailable to many Boltonians in the 1800s.

Tiny cottages built for workers, could house several families, some living in the damp cellars. In the 1800s in cities such as Manchester and Liverpool, one family or even two could be crammed into a single cellar dwelling. This was at a time when families consisted of typically nine to ten members, and possibly more. In London, tens of thousands of people slept in bunks in verminous lodging houses for which they paid two pence a night. Others, for half the price, slept on kitchen floors, while those even more unfortunates 'made do' with sleeping rough in cellars shared with pigs (Hibbert, 1977;

Morley, 1971). Quite apart from the depressing effects, which overcrowding and poor housing may have had on the workers, such conditions had disastrous effects on people's health. When large numbers of people lived together in close proximity, without proper drainage or sanitation, contagious diseases, such as smallpox, typhus, cholera, influenza and tuberculosis were rife.

Conditions for the poor in the North of England were no better than anywhere else. Poverty had always been a strong feature of Lancashire life. In the sixteenth and seventeenth centuries, there were vast areas of potentially rich farmland that remained uncultivated, although for those who did farm the land, life could be quite comfortable. Communication with other areas was limited because there were few roads and illiteracy was widespread. For the poor, life had become increasingly harsh following the Reformation and the closure of the monasteries and abbeys. These had provided hospitals and almshouses, which had given vital support to the communities. Following the Reformation, the poor had no provision made for them at all.

Some people lacked even the most basic possessions required to survive or to live a social life. In the 1600s for example, two women from a parish in Lancashire had been excused from church attendance because they had no clothes to wear. One of the Lancaster witches, Demdike had also been confined to her house for a period because she had only a single garment (Bennett, 1957).

Followers of the Church of England had little compassion for the poor whom they believed could emancipate themselves with sufficient effort and hard work. Protestants disapproved strongly of the ignorance and high rates of illegitimacy, which they observed in the lower classes, and felt no obligation to help those for whom they had no regard. So the poor had to make a living by whatever means they could; working as labourers, carding and spinning wool, begging, poaching and stealing.

However, even during such difficult times, life in Bolton for most of its inhabitants had been comparatively prosperous. As early as 1770, Bolton had become nationally renowned for various textile products, such as cotton, velvets, muslins and wool. Bolton had been a market town since 1251, forming a focal point for the surrounding hamlets in a comparatively sparsely populated area. Innovations in the development of textile machinery,[2] together with developments in coal-powered machines, which were able to produce artificial energy, meant that Bolton's enterprises were well situated and very successful. Bolton was conveniently placed for easy access to the surrounding areas. Situated as it is in a basin, Bolton's climate is ideal for the production of cotton. From being centred on two streets, Deansgate and Bradshawgate, the town mushroomed and spread to enclose nearby settlements. Between 1773 and 1871 the population grew from 5,000 to 22,000. Service industries, such as shops and banks were on the increase by the 1870s, forming part of a maturing economy.

By the early 1800s, Lancashire was recognised by the rest of England, as the premier county of wealth, famous for the magnitude of its business undertakings. The industries that developed in the area included ship-building, iron and steel, glass production, chemicals, leather, pottery and engineering. In order to support and ensure that the efficiency of these industries was maintained, related systems of transport and communication developed, including improved coach roads, railways and canal systems. Nineteenth century Lancashire was accessible and attractive, in terms of employment opportunities, and it became a focal point to which immigrants from far and wide were drawn (Johnson, 1996).

Bolton fared particularly well during this time of prosperity, and standards of living for middle-class Boltonians improved steadily. Middle-class Bolton families lived in impressive Georgian homes. Some examples of this type of accommodation, although now primarily occupied by businesses, still exist in areas such as Mawdsley Street, Silverwell Street and Wood Street. Other middle-class people moved out of the town centre into semi-detached villas,

---

2   Some of these had been developed by local people such as Samuel Crompton.

surrounded by gardens and situated in areas such as Chorley New Road (Gent, 1995).

Life for the workers, however, was far from prosperous (Johnson, 1996). The industrial towns of Lancashire, including Bolton, offered only overcrowded housing, low pay and disease. Conditions were harsh for men and women. Regardless of marital status, working-class women worked full-time in the new industries, just like the men (Kenny, 1994). Women and children worked as drawers in the coal mines.[3] It was common for husband and wife teams to work together down the mine. The wife would work in this capacity, as her husband's 'drawer'. This continued until nineteenth century religious reformers, expressing moral concerns about men and women working together down the pit, stopped the practice (John, 1992). Following this, women were replaced in the mines by pit ponies.

Religion, poverty and working-class solidarity

Racial prejudice developed as the population of the town increased with an influx of people from Ireland, Scotland and Wales. The main targets of racism in the 1800s were the Irish. The rise of Catholicism in Bolton was not only associated with the number of Irish residents, but their presence was a source of concern. Drunkenness observed during Irish wakes appears to have reinforced the widely accepted stereotype of 'drunken Irishmen.' The 'Hungry Forties' led to an even greater influx of Irish people into the town. Outbreaks of typhus, nicknamed 'Irish Fever' were attributed to Irish immigrants. Dale (1985) argues that, although religious and racial bigotry did exist, it was less apparent in the lower-classes. This may have been due to the strong working-class solidarity of the time. The poor were poor no matter what their origins and, although there were riots caused by industrial and political issues, outbreaks stemming from racist or religious bigotry were rare. Religious effigies were burned on some occasions and

---

3   A 'drawer' was a person employed to pull the crates of coal (Dale, 1985).

letters from anti-Catholic writers appeared in local papers, expressing disapproval for the 'Beasts of Babylon.'

In rougher areas, gangs of working-class youths spent their leisure time, seeking out Irish immigrants to tease and bait. This was unlikely to been motivated by any real sense of malice. Such activities represented the kind of 'entertainment' popular in a subculture where drinking and brawling formed the basis of working-class masculine identity. Even when apparent, bigotry in Bolton was mild compared to other areas. In Wigan, for example, the walls of some Irish Catholic areas had been covered with the slogan 'Hell and Purgatory to the Papists'. Overall, the population of Bolton included people from diverse geographic origins and religious affiliations who worked and lived together in relative harmony (Dale, 1985).

Bolton workers lived in crowded back-to-back houses. In 1845, 4,961 people in Bolton lived in 1,210 cellars (Gent, 1995). One of the older women interviewed by Kenny (aged 86 years in 1989) recalled how one of her sisters lodged in a cellar dwelling shortly after her marriage. The woman described how depressing, cramped and damp the cellar was. The 'last straw' for the sister came when she woke up to find a rat on the hearth rug beside the bed. Fortunately, the woman's sister had a supportive family, willing to offer her a home until she was able to find more suitable accommodation. The woman interviewed explained that her sister's husband was away at the time, fighting in the First World War. It seems clear from this interview that people still lived in cellars in Bolton until the early 1920s.

There is a tendency to romanticise the 'good old days' when, following a death, bodies were laid out and kept in the home until the time of burial. During an epidemic, families stored up to three corpses at any one time, in these tiny houses or cellars (Morley, 1971). The bereaved family's desire to provide a good funeral could delay the removal of corpses. Newspaper reports of the time provide useful information about the conditions in which people lived during the 1800s. A reporter from a local newspaper who visited the home of a cholera victim during the epidemic of 1832, wrote:[4]

4   *Bolton Chronicle*, August 25th, 1832.

'The house itself was in a very filthy state, and quite
likely from the number of people living in it and the bad
ventilation, to give rise to an epidemic of formidable
character'.

Such conditions clearly had implications for public health, but
the problem was compounded for the poor because they could
not afford a reasonable diet. Poor nutrition meant that people
were more susceptible to, and less able to resist, infectious
diseases. The subculture in which drink played a large part,
did not help matters. Hibbert writes that when a working man
socialised, it was expected that he should buy a round of
drinks, regardless of his ability to pay. The purchase of alcohol
by the poor became widespread following the Chancellor of the
Exchequer's removal of tax on beer and cider in 1830.
Following this act, the trade in alcohol was more open. For a
fee of only two guineas, all householders had the right to sell
beer from their premises.

There was a rapid increase in alehouses following the act
and, by the year 1848, there were over 300 in Bolton. In 1867,
an editorial in a Methodist paper reflected a national concern
for the dangers of 'demon drink.' Calls for legislative action
were made on the grounds that 'Drunkenness has been for
ages the vice of Englishmen.' Concern for the 'evils' caused by
drink led to the formation of the temperance movement, the
founder in Bolton in 1840 being a man called Joseph Livessey.
This was followed by the founding of the Catholic Temperance
Society in 1848, by a Father Matthew. The concerns of the
temperance workers were well founded. Drink had been the
cause, directly and indirectly, of several deaths in the town.
These included suicides, homicides and accidental deaths
(Dale, *op cit*).

The temperance workers occupied a role similar to that
of social workers today. Many worked with families in which
poverty and discord could be, at least partly, attributed to the
presence of one, or even two alcoholics. Contact with the poor,
made even poorer by the consumption of alcohol, led to an
evangelic approach in which the fight against 'demon drink'
developed into a crusade. Speeches from reformed drunks,
such as Temperance Bob, formally Drunken Bob, added to the
enthusiasm of the meetings. Topics covered in a series of

lectures held in Bolton Temperance Hall in 1841 (cited in Dale, 1985) were:

1. The ignorance of the juvenile population where the parents spend money on drink rather than their betterment.

2. Half filled chapels compared to full public houses.

3. Families living in poor houses and cellars who had the means of bettering themselves but preferred to spend the money on drink.

Despite the charismatic and evangelical spirit of the movement, temperance workers appear to have taken a balanced, non-judgmental approach to the problems they encountered. This was largely because they understood the conditions that encouraged alcohol consumption. People did not necessarily drink for entertainment, or as a form of escapism. Alcohol was cheaper than coffee or tea and cleaner than the filthy water available from the public taps. The majority of people drank ale simply because they were thirsty. The temperance workers acknowledged this and responded in a practical way. Temperance bars sold cheap lemonade and raspberry vinegar.

Several of the older Boltonian women interviewed, spoke of the temperance bars of the 1930s and 1950s, so it seems that the movement remained active in the town for over a hundred years. Time spent in the temperance bars was very enjoyable for the young. One of the women (aged 84 years when interviewed in 1989) explained that pubs in her youth, were for old people.

In the 1800s, alcoholism could be caused by, rather than be the cause, of poverty — the chicken and egg situation. Lodgings used by the poor in cities such as London, were so appalling that many felt the need for a glass of gin, before they could face the prospect of sleeping in them. But money spent on alcohol could lead to reduced spending on good food. The following report expresses concern about the diet of the poor:

> '*in all of these cases (of cholera) the predisposing factors appear to be a want of sufficient food, and those necessary comforts upon which depend human existence and,*

*further, that the outbreak of cholera in the town appeared
to be caused more through want than the strength and
virulence of the disease.'*

Examination of other newspaper reports of the 1800s supports
evidence of the scale of poverty endured by many Boltonians.
The oral and written testimonies of many older people of the
town suggest that conditions had not improved much, by the
middle of this century. Joe Clarke for example, remembered
from his childhood:[5]

*'Cockers chip shop on Ellesmere Street at closing time.
Mr Cocker would send the family any left-overs for free
which all the boys looked forward to.'*

*He also remembers that as a young lad, he would go up to
the Salvation Army place with a great big jug for
two-pence, 'it was filled with soup and dumplings'. Joe
tells me that many of the poorer families in Farnworth
were also dependent on the Salvation Army's help. 'They
kept those streets going.'*

Tom Mcfarlane, also remembered Farnworth of the 1930s:[6]

*'The work available was slave labour, long hours and
very little pay.'*

In the 1930s, the problem for most workers was the severe
menace to health caused by the terrible working conditions in
the pits.

*'"There would be many more lads of my age today" says
Tom "most of them were told they had bronchitis, but it
was pneumoconiosis, a real killer, that was the real
problem. If this had been diagnosed, they'd have been
given a decent pension, and they would have had a better
standard of living while they were ill." Tom also recalled
how "many of the poorer children didn't even have a pair
of clogs and that a charity would come round and supply*

5   Clarke J (1996) Surviving the hard times. In: *Living Around Here.*
     Stories from the area around the New Bury Community Centre.
     New Bury Community Centre, Buckley Lane, Bolton, No 5

6   Mcfarlane T (1996) Tom and company. In: *Living Around Here (op
     cit)*

> *'coal boats'. These were great big heavy clogs that came right up their legs, they looked like something that Mr Frankenstein's monster wears and these were little kids with skinny legs.'"*

Yet despite the poverty endured by the working-classes, care, mutual support and respect were evident in many of the communities. Jarvis (1907), in his experiences as a Victorian detective, wrote that:

> *'Poverty is a hard lot, and it would be a hopeless despair were it not for the kindness of the poor to the poor.'*

The kindness of the poor to the poor is a recurring theme in this book. In a social context, the perceived importance of a decent burial was linked with rising mortality and the impossibility of maintaining dignity in life led to a desire to at least achieve it in death. Kindness and goodwill among working-class people became a necessary survival mechanism.

It would be wrong to assume that the inadequate planning of new towns could be attributed only to wilful neglect by employers and town planners. Some of the planning inadequacies were caused by ignorance of the ways in which contagious diseases were transmitted. Prior to the development of the germ theory at the beginning of the twentieth century, diseases were believed to be contained in airborne clouds called miasma.

Unaware of the dangers of infection, people did not interprete unpleasant smells as we would today. A smelly drain, for example, indicated a change in the weather and people were grateful to be given a warning. Misunderstandings of this type may have had their origins in the years of the Black Death. During this time it was noticed that the attendants who took care of the latrines and who served in hospitals appeared to escape infection. This observation caused many citizens of plague struck cities to spend hours each day leaning over a latrine, inhaling for medicinal purposes, the foul smells from below (Ziegler, 1969).

However, before the germ theory became known, some speculative links were made about the connection between cleanliness and health. Reports of the 1832 cholera outbreak noted that:

'strong predisposing causes for the disease are produced by distress and a want of proper attention to cleanliness.'

A few weeks later it was further reported that:[7]

'a correspondent informs us that it has been ascertained that a certain remedy for the cholera, and one that has never failed in any one instance in which it has been tried in time, is to drink water as hot as can be borne by the patient. It produces a speedy reaction to the system and the patient then recovers from the severity of the attack.'

Most readers will know that boiling water can kill some germs. Thus, any recovery in the patients observed was probably due to drinking cleaner water. Limitations of health knowledge in the 1800s, meant that rich and poor were at risk of developing contagious diseases from the filth of the towns. Despite such ignorance, there still appeared to be a lack of concern, or care on the part of the middle- and ruling-classes, for the working-class population.

The middle- and upper-classes, did not have an already difficult position compounded by the effects of a poor diet, overcrowding and lack of access to medical and nursing care. Indeed, during the nineteenth century, the middle-classes enjoyed a reduction in mortality rates that the working-classes did not share (Houlbrooke, 1989). Medical and scientific theories that developed during the nineteenth century, did not necessarily improve matters for the working-class.

Some scientific theories of the time claimed that class differences had a biological basis and that some people were 'naturally' superior or inferior to others. Darwin's Theory of Evolution provides an example of how nineteenth century 'scientific' theories could indirectly justify social, gender and racial inequalities. Disraeli in his novel 'Sibyl' argued that Queen Victoria reigned over two nations:

'between whom there is no intercourse and no sympathy, who are as ignorant of each others habits, thoughts and feelings, as if they were habitants of different planets,

7   *Bolton Chronicle*, September 1st, 1832.

*who are formed by different breeding, fed by different
food, ordered by different manners and governed by
different laws. They are the rich and poor'*

(cited by Hibbert, 1977).

Social conditions, commnunity health and the burial crisis of the 1800s

The conditions in which the poor had to live were challenged
by reformers who contributed, in their own individual and
collective ways, to raising awareness and changing for the
better (at least in the material sense) the situation of the poor.
Reformers such as Chadwick, however, who campaigned for
improved sanitation, faced passionate opposition.

In Birmingham, proposals to appoint sanitary inspectors
were opposed on the grounds that they were too expensive to
employ. There were also fears and suspicions about the powers
such authorities might have. Plans proposed in Sheffield in
1860, to develop more efficient and improved sewage systems
were delayed until 1884 (Hibbert, 1977). In 1845, the Trusties
of Little Bolton held a special meeting to discuss the Sewage
and Drainage Bill that had been introduced into the House of
Commons in 1844.[8] The purpose of the meeting was to discuss:

*'Reference to their provision, or any of them being applied
to the town of Bolton.'*

Assumptions made at the meeting include that:

*'where townships were in a real state, it was probable that
they might be brought under its protection, but if
townships were in a good state of sewage and drainage,
no interference would be made.'*

Basically, the conclusion of Little Bolton Trusties was that:

*'Little Bolton was in a good position and it would be
premature for them to interfere with the business at
present.'*

The rationale for excluding outside 'interference' was that:

8   *Bolton Free Press*, 18th October, 1845.

> *'the Trusties are acting on some principles as to the form of sewage, as would be required by the bill and that it intended therein to do the same.'*

The report included a reminder to readers that:

> *'the Trusties were appointed by the rate payers in a fair and frank manner, and that they could do no better than have the spending of their own money.'*

This is an interesting point when one considers that only two months later, complaints were to be made in the same paper about the filthy state of Bolton's streets.

The report concluded by stating that, in relation to the proposed Sewage and Drainage Bill:

> *'it is resolved that the trusties of little Bolton take no part at present in any further Parliamentary or other measure for investigating the town council for any additional powers for further improving and regulating the borough of Bolton.'*

As mortality rates in towns and cities increased with the growth in population, a national burial crisis arose in the mid nineteenth century. The burial grounds of small parish churches had been designed to accommodate the dead from small rural communities. By the mid nineteenth century, these burial grounds were crammed with corpses. The level of the grounds steadily rose above the surrounding houses.

These overcrowded burial grounds provided another source of contamination. Water draining from them flowed into the nearby rivers. The sough from human remains soon filtered into drinking water and sewers. Samuel Pills (cited by Kelly, 1988) described one London chapel where, following the laying of a sewer, rubbish, including human bones and flesh in various states of putrefaction flowed into the surrounding streets. Corpses, separated from the public by only a thin piece of wood rested beneath the chapel and in the burial grounds. Pills estimated that there would be an average of 12,000 bodies buried within a space of 59 feet by 29 feet. Surrounding the burial ground on three sides were houses, and waste from the burial grounds oozed into the kitchens and cellars (Kelly, 1988).

Inadequate burial of the dead posed an even greater threat during epidemics. Grave diggers from one chapel in Manchester, during an outbreak of cholera, dumped corpses and buckets of rotting human remains from old graves, into a nearby river (Kelly, 1988). The burial crisis appears to have effected Bolton badly. In 1849 complaints were made by members of the local community around Pilkington Street, of an 'evil smell' coming from Saint Peter and Paul's Catholic Church. The source of the stench was a large vault in the chapel yard containing between 20 and 30 corpses, covered by only a few boards. The priest, although sympathetic, realised that the cost of single graves was beyond the financial means of many poor people. However, mass pauper graves posed serious health risks because these were left open until full. It was not long before the presence of such unburied corpses began to cause trouble (Dale, 1985). But the problem was not confined to Saint Peter and Paul's Church.

Kelly, drawing on the work of Rothwell and Entwistle, describes how some houses had been built so close to graveyards that coffins were resting against the cellar walls. Drainage oozed from these burial grounds, filtered through the foundations of nearby houses, causing a stench from beneath the flagstones which many of the habitants found intolerable. As the population of the town grew so, too, did the problem. The height of burial grounds in Bolton churches began to rise above the surrounding streets. During more recent times, many Boltonians felt uneasy about possible health risks posed by the presence of graveyards. One of the woman interviewed spoke of her late grandfather, who had often expressed concern about the height of graveyards. He believed, intuitively, and without any scientific knowledge to support his view, that if graveyards rose above the surrounding houses, this could effect the local drinking water. One row of cottages in the Edgeworth area had the nickname, 'the graveyard' which suggests that they may have been situated quite near a burial ground.[9] However, few Bolton

9   *Bolton Free Press*, 1844, 23rd November, article titled 'Graveyard Cottages for Sale'.

people viewed cremation as an alternative to burial until the latter half of the twentieth century.

Apart from the problems caused by unhygienic disposal of the dead, many homeless and vagrant people became ill and died in the streets. Once found, the bodies of such unfortunates would be transported to the nearest public house. Here it was left to wait for inspection by the coroner or surgeon (see the case of Old Tom, *Chapter 8*). Many of these public houses served food as well as drink. One can only speculate with horror, on the risks to health of storing a corpse for several days or weeks in the back room of a public house. Some poor families would abandon the bodies of their dead children in the street rather than endure the humiliation of having to bury them in a pauper's grave (Morley, 1971). The dead are disposed of in such a clinical way these days, that it seems hard to imagine a time when corpses could be found scattered around the streets, together with other types of rubbish and decaying matter. Indeed, during the last century, dead bodies could often 'pop up' in some of the most unexpected places. A local newspaper in 1831, for example reported that:[10]

> *'On Tuesday last, as some farmers were emptying the necessary belonging to the Coach and Horse, Deansgate, they turned up the body of a man, which appeared from the state of decomposition which it was in, to have been embedded in the soil for some time.'*

Meg Parkinson, the landlady, suggested that the copse may have belonged to a William Mooney, who was last seen, very drunk, about two years before the discovery in the midden. Mooney had been refused entry into the Coach and Horses because he had called after closing time. Meg reported that she had watched Mooney as he walked away from her window and recalled seeing him bend over the necessary. It was established that the body was Mooney's by his landlady, who based her identification on shoes worn by the corpse. Mr Adrian Watson, the surgeon who examined the body reported that:

10   *Bolton Chronicle*, February 19th, 1831.

'I examined the body of the man found in Mrs. Parkinson's midden stead, but it was in such a state of decomposition that it was impossible to say whether the deceased died of violence or not. The head was separated from the body, which I could say was caused by decomposition. There was very little flesh remaining on the bones. My opinion is that the deceased fell forward in the midden stead, and sank to the bottom where he was kept down by the weight of the soil upon him.'

What is a necessary, or midden stead? When one of the authors asked her older relatives about this, she was informed by some that it was a kind of dustbin, while others described it as a type of cesspool. Given that Mr Mooney had been last seen bending over the necessary, it is possible that this necessary, at least, doubled as a public lavatory. Mr Mooney had last been seen two years prior to the body being found in the necessary. So, it is clear that emptying such waste containers was not given high priority in 1831 and may well have been highly contagious sources of infection.

In conclusion, rising populations in the towns and cities, high mortality rates, poor living conditions and sanitary provision, as well as inefficient disposal of the dead, led to demands for change by reformers, demands that were increasingly successful. Social reforms led to the provision of cleaner water, adequate drainage and sanitation and a cleaner and pleasanter environment. Improved housing, nutrition and the medical and social innovations implemented since the turn of the century have led to greater longevity. Concerns about the hygienic disposal of the dead led to the development of clinical and efficient technologies and storage systems. The dead are now transferred to hygienic temperature-controlled storage rooms in mortuaries and funeral parlours. These changes have made a difference, not only to the quality of life for the living, but also to death rituals, funeral practices and to the way we perceive death. Unlike our forbears, we are no longer constantly reminded of our mortality by the visible and enduring presence of the dead. Nationally and locally, public health and changing social concerns and fashions have had 'knock-on' effects on death rituals and funerals. These effects will be discussed further in *Chapter 9*.

Chapter 2
Religion, culture and death in the north west

Both culture and religion have a strong impact on our perceptions and attitudes towards death and, in turn, on the practices and rituals observed. Much of the behaviour associated with death is shaped by beliefs related to the supernatural and the occult. A woman interviewed for this study, explained how some West Indian and Nigerian people respond to confrontations with death: [1]

Interviewee: well a lot of West Indian people, like for arguments sake, when I told my mother that I was working in the mortuary, she said 'well don't go near the doppies, they call them doppies' I mean for a lot of West Indian and Nigerian people, just mention a mortuary and they just freak out. I mean, you have to have special baths and showers, and water has to be treated in special ways, and all this before you handle or go near the dead. To a certain extent I am superstitious. But I think that the living can hurt you much more than the dead. The thing that I do get nervous about is handling dead babies. We believe that the spirit of a dead baby is more powerful than the spirit of an adult. I treat all of the bodies with respect, but I am extra careful when I handle a dead baby.'

Many people, no matter how well educated have similar fears relating to the dead. Much of this fear, or awe, is caused by religious beliefs. Christianity, like most post-modern religions, has amalgamated ancient pagan beliefs into its teaching. It is this amalgam of belief within religion that is explored in this chapter. Dale (1985) writes that that the town of Bolton has a very rich and diverse religious history. Dale's book provides an account of the growth of religion in Bolton since the Industrial Revolution. The author, in this book, although focusing

1   Interviews with employers who work in a hospital mortuary

mainly on Bolton, takes a wider view of the North and begins her exploration from an earlier starting point in time. This chapter explores, not only the origins of the more established religions, but also those pagan religions that drew on the influence of belief in witchcraft and magic. This is because the authors are aware that pagan beliefs continue to influence death rituals and, as the discussion will show, religious beliefs in the North.

Parkes *et al* (1997) write that the word 'religion' is taken from the Latin word 'religare' which means 'to bind.' They define culture as the 'social heritage of a community' and 'the sum total of possessions, ways of thinking and behaviour that distinguish one group of people from another'. Collectively, these are transferred from one generation to another. Culture and religion influence each other, but religion can be shared across cultures. All religious people have a belief in a source of divine power(s) of which singular or multiple god(s) have the monopoly. Nearly all major religions of the present day have a male god, although this has not always been the case. In ancient times, most pagan religions had equal numbers of male and female gods and some gave their faith to a single female god. The God of the early Christian Church, although portrayed as male, had a personality now described as androgynous. In other words, the early Christian God had as many feminine, as masculine characteristics (Achterberg, 1990). Evidence of an androgynous God is present in parts of the New Testament and in the teachings of Jesus of Nazareth. The Roman Catholic Church is the only contemporary religion that retains a strong feminine influence. It is this feminine element which has led certain writers (not all of them Catholic or even religious) to argue that Catholicism offers the most promising religious basis on which to build any politics of peace (Galtung, 1996).

Religions disseminate across cultures and diversity is common, even in the major religions. Parkes *et al* state that a cynical writer once said of Hinduism that 'the only thing Hindus have in common is their Indian nationality and their veneration for the cow.' In situations where people of a wide range of religious affiliations work and live together, it is common to adopt an eclectic approach. Religious differences can lead to conflict, but, more frequently, diversity in religious beliefs increases tolerance and harmony between groups (Parkes *et al* 1997).

In small scale societies governed by natural forces, such as the weather, it is common for people to worship several gods, each representing some aspect of nature. Shamanism is a religious philosophy and healing practice based on pagan religion. Shaman healers still exist in many societies, sharing a usually amicable existence with contemporary religions and medical practices. Shaman healers adopt a holistic approach and believe that maintaining the balance and well-being of mind, body and spirit is of equal importance. For the shaman, affinity with nature, as opposed to the conquest and control of nature, is fundamental to the healing process. Healing need not necessarily mean the prevention of a death, but rather, enabling the sick person to come to terms with it and to meet it with dignity and the minimum of discomfort. Because of the emphasis on spirituality, healing and religious practice involves much ritual, often facilitated by bringing about altered states of consciousness. Drugs may help to bring about these altered states of consciousness, together with fasting, perceptual deprivation, chanting and the worship of animal spirits on whose power the shaman hopes to draw.

Animal spirits are worshipped across cultures. The Eskimo worships the great white whale, the American Indian the bear, buffalo and the eagle and the European worships the cat and the snake. In England, the dog and the hare also appear to have been animal spirits who were much revered by the early pagans (Acterberg, 1985). Shaman and small-scale religions appear, in general, to revere the dead, who enjoy a strong presence among the living, particularly if they are ancestors. In this context, the deceased may be regarded as alive long after the time when a westerner will consider them to be dead. Funeral practices involve care and homage to the long dead, as well as to the recently deceased (Rosenblatt, 1997).

Pagan religion was followed by the major religions of the world, such as Buddhism, Hinduism, Islam, Judaism and Christianity. In Bolton during the twentieth century, there has been an influx of multi-denominational religious groups.

This has created even greater cultural diversity and has un-
doubtedly influenced the Christian religions, which dominated in the previous centuries. These later influences are not
explored in this book. The author has compiled a thanatology
of the North, up to the 1990s. Her analysis is based on a
history of pagan and Christian religions, and is an exploration
of the ways in which these have become interwoven over the
years, thus shaping death rituals and practice.

All Christian religions are based on the teachings of
Jesus, a Jewish lay healer and preacher who lived around
AD30. Christians believe that Jesus was the son of God, who
died on the cross, but was later resurrected and ascended to
heaven. The teachings of Jesus Christ were recorded by his
disciples and form the basis of the New Testament. The early
Christians struggled at first with the question of how to
reconcile the human persona of Jesus with that of an all
powerful, singular and supernatural God. This problem was
overcome with the creation of the Holy Trinity that
symbolises the union of God the Father, God the Son and God
the Holy Spirit. In the Christian church, Jesus the son of God,
who took human form during his time on earth, is honoured
together with his father (Blanche and Parkes, 1997). Jesus'
mother Mary is also revered and, through her, the
reproductive and creative potential of women. However,
unlike the early pagan religions, where women's sexuality was
revered and, indeed, celebrated, Mary's sexuality is idealised
and in many ways muted. Relatively scant attention is paid to
Jesus' earthly father, St Joseph. This could be due to the
difficulty of Jesus having two fathers, one on earth and
another in heaven — Mary has no heavenly rivals.

The early Christians who were persecuted by the
Romans, clearly had a very strong faith in salvation after
death. When put to the lions, these Christians died so bravely
that witnesses to the events exclaimed in astonishment
'behold how they die' (Pojman, 1992). For the early
Christians, death had a different meaning. It had a sacred
element driven by the model of Christ. The death of Jesus was
a reconciling death, offering a means of mediating a blessing to
humankind. Thus, according to Davis (1988), the death of

Christ 'established the new and eternal communication with a humanity cleansed from sin with its God.'

According to Blanche and Parkes (*op cit*), the Emperor Constantine adopted Christianity in AD313. After this it spread throughout the Roman Empire and then the world. As Christianity became more widespread it became more diverse. Despite attempts to maintain some uniformity, Christianity broke into various subsections. At large scale, level two, the major breaks with the Roman Catholic Church came with the establishment of the Eastern Orthodox religions and the Protestant Reformation.

Until very recent times in Bolton, Christianity in all its various forms has been the dominant religious influence. However, as we will discuss at a later stage in this chapter, Christianity in the North was shaded by the pagan religions which preceded Christianity. Prior to the Protestant Reformation, Catholicism was the dominant faith. There is very little difference in religious beliefs between the Catholics and Protestants, or in this case, the Church of England. The Pope is the head of the Catholic Church. The Monarchy is the head of the Church of England. The bread and wine taken in a Catholic communion are the blood and flesh of Christ. For Protestants, bread and wine symbolise the blood and flesh of Christ. This is one example of how differences brought about by the Reformation reflected attempts to take the 'magical' element of religion. Other Christian religions which developed in Bolton during the Industrial Revolution include the Methodist, Unitarian and Quaker. The North has a fascinating history of religion and death rituals. We begin our discussion of established religion around the 1500s. But we also acknowledge in our analysis, the pagan religions which came before.

Pagan beliefs that the early missionaries were at pains to eradicate, shaded the early Christian faith. The singular and relatively humane God worshipped by the early Christians was a novelty to ancient people. Compared to the awesome and all powerful Greek and Roman gods, the Christian God seemed hardly worth serious consideration (Davis, 1988). The challenge facing missionaries of the early church, was that they needed to persuade converts that they were 'signing up' in effect, to a more powerful source of magic. Like all things in life, in order to 'take off' Christianity needed to be saying the right thing at the right time. Around the time of the Emperor Constantine people must have been looking for some new hope. This new hope came in the form the teachings of Jesus. Much of the recorded words of Christ have the same 'flavour' that the early Enlightenment had — the idea of the dawning of a new age. For example, the following quote from Luke (X1: 20): 'If I by the finger of God, cast out devils then is the kingdom of God come upon you.' This 'exorcism' promised by Christianity marked, as Davis (1988) has noted, the suggestion of some driving force which would wage a powerful assault on the forces of evil. This affront to the forces of evil, plus the cleansing possibilities brought about by the death of Christ, offered a very powerful magic indeed. Unlike the all powerful and sometimes punitive Ancient Gods of Greece and Rome, here was the promise of a deity who was willing to form a union with (as opposed to the conquest of) humankind. And for the privilege of enjoying his protection, this powerful get kindly God only asked for his appeasement that human beings should love each other.[2]

The claim to supernatural power was an essential element in the Anglo-Saxon churches. The ability to perform miracles and healing was an indispensable test of sanctity and the missionaries stressed to converts, the supremacy of Christian prayers to heathen charms (Thomas, 1971). Possession of children could be 'cured' by a godly minister who could also perform exorcisms to rid house and neighbourhood from a whole range of devils, demons, evil spirits and goblins.

Religion, superstition and death rituals in Lancashire

By the time of the Reformation, pagan belief and established religion had become totally confused. A poor witch in the North, if cursing someone would often 'threaten' to pray for them. The Old Testament may have caused some of the

2   This is why Christians pray for the salvation and protection of the departed and expect these prayers to be answered. Christians believe that the power of love is greater than the power of death (Zernou, 1988).

confusion between charm and prayer. It is written in the book of Exodus that those who are unkind to the poor or to children would provoke God's wrath (Hasted, 1993). Small pieces of parchment designed to ward off evil spirits, could have written on them names of the Trinity and of Greek and Romans gods, planets, mystical signs and Latin prayers. Even a Monk of Whalley thought it well worth his while to wear a charm to protect him against a whole range of ills from toothache to bleeding (Bennett, 1957). In most pagan religions, good and evil is believed to reside within a single deity. The creation of a God who was completely good and virtuous required some explanation for the presence of evil in the world. For the Christian Church this explanation came with the creation of the devil. The Devil seduced people into a life of sin and had the responsibility of confining the sinner's soul in hell for all eternity, and of applying a variety of tortures. Demons, evil spirits and goblins were enlisted to help him. Thomas (1971: 559) writes:

> *'Relatively unimportant in the Old Testament, Satan had been raised by later Judaism and Christianity to the status of God's grand cosmic antagonist. He was an omnipresent force, ever ready to prey upon man's weaker instincts and to tempt him away into paths of evil. He was also an instrument of God's judgement, for the sinners of this world constituted members of Satan's kingdom after their death. In Hell they were subjected to undying torments over which he presided.'*

Aries (1974) portrays the dominant attitude to death at this time, as one of quiet acceptance. But this may be a distortion, because belief in the devil must have made death a terrible prospect for the sinner who could never be completely sure of absolution (forgiveness from God). For those whose sins in life had not been evil enough to warrant condemnation to eternal damnation, there was purgatory. Purgatory was a dimensional plane resting somewhere between heaven and hell. It provided an interval plane in which the sinner could wait until prayers said by the chantry priests were sufficient to allow his or her entrance into Heaven.

Inevitably, this led to confusion between Christianity and paganism among the poor at least, who honoured the church without having any real understanding of its doctrines (Hasted, 1985). In England, such confusion was common in remote areas such as Lancashire. The situation may have been exacerbated by the Reformation because the Protestant Church placed an even greater emphasis on the evil influence of the Devil. For example, Luther often spoke as if everything in the physical world, especially the flesh, was owned by the Devil. Nevertheless, the Protestant Church was committed to removing the magic from religion but, with the influence of Catholicism still very strong, this proved very difficult. The Reformation made Catholicism illegal, thus driving it underground. The influence of any movement that is driven underground, tends to become more, rather than less powerful. The potential for misinterpretation also increases. Because it was illegal following the Reformation, it is difficult to know how many Catholics continued to practice under cover. Records of the time suggest that many northerners were very reluctant to give up the old religion.

At the time of the Reformation, the spiritual climate of Lancashire was causing London a great deal of concern. Although belief in magic was quite widespread throughout England, it was in Lancashire, specifically, that religious practices were believed to be pagan and lawless. Belief that the county was a resort for witches was strong. Thomas Potts, clerk of the court at the Pendle Witch Trials noted that it was a vast area and a most suitable habitat for witches. In 1628 Sir Benjamin Rudyard had spoke of the 'utmost skirts of the north, where prayers of the common people are more like spells and charms than devotions' (Thomas, 1971: 73). The assumption that the practice of Catholicism was widespread in the area was not helped by the fact that the poor in the north continued to sign themselves with the cross and to use it as a symbol to ward off evil. In numerous attempts to counteract the problem, orders were sent from London for justices of the peace (JPs) to arrest those who did not attend the established church and to round up all Catholics and priests. For the most part, these orders fell on deaf ears. JPs in the north, who did not share the Southerners fears or perception of a Catholic 'problem', had no motivation for persecuting their friends and neighbours because of a difference in religious opinion.

Anti-Catholicism in politics came to a head with the Gunpowder Plot. There was a widespread belief that the Plot was part of a Catholic conspiracy and further, that it was constructed by Catholics in the north. This paranoia and the publication of James I's 'Daemonologie' led to the Pendle Witch Trials. Although it is true that the witch craze was well established, there is much evidence to suggest that the Pendle Witch Trials were highly political. Alice Nutter, one of the women convicted, was a known practising and very devout Catholic. Two of her relatives had been executed as Jesuit priests some years prior to 1612, the year of the trials. There was some consternation at the time of Alice Nutter's conviction because she did not fit the stereotype of a witch, being a well-educated woman of considerable wealth. Potts observed that 'she was a rich woman, had great estate and children of good hope' and that she was 'of good temper, free from envy and malice.' Alice was implicated in the trial because she had been seen visiting some of the other women charged. Alice did not explain why she had spent time in their company and refused to say anything at all during her trial. It is now speculated that she may have called on the poorer convicted women in order to offer them assistance, a theory consistent with Catholic practice at the time. Alice may have made this call on her way to a Catholic meeting. She may have refused to speak because of fear that she might incriminate her Catholic friends (Bennett, 1957; Hasted, 1993). Potts stated that Alice Nutter's 'own children were never able to move her to confess any particular offence or declare anything, even when about to die.'

The Pendle Witches present an example of how confused pagan and Christian practice and belief had become by the 1600s. These women, convicted of witchcraft and executed in 1612, are famous in the history of Lancashire. In all, thirteen women were sent to trial. Three were acquitted, one died in prison, one was punished in the pillory, followed by imprisonment, and eight were executed. Following the executions and convictions, their stories passed into folklore and later caught the imagination of writers of the Romantic period, such as Sir Walter Scott. Over the years, different theories and stereotypes about the Pendle Witches have developed and there has been speculation that at least some of them may have been lay healers. Whether or not the Pendle women were healers in the shaman tradition is difficult to say. There is certainly ample evidence that they were fond of animals and often made models and images of their pets. It was this practice, among others, that led to their conviction. Most of the women confessed to having a familiar, or animal spirit companion at their trial.

Of the two older witches, Mother Chattox is reported as having a familiar called 'Fancy' who appeared to her sometimes as a dog, sometimes as a black cat. The second of the older women, Demdike had a familiar called 'Tibb' who appeared to her on some occasions as a small boy and on others as a black dog or cat. It seems likely from the few records in existence, that the women did experience altered states of consciousness from time to time, and that they also subscribed to pagan beliefs. But clearly, they were also devout Christians. They used prayer and religious symbols, such as the sign of the cross, to bless and/or protect themselves, their kin and their property. As for their association with the dead, in *Chapter 3*, it is suggested that much of the knowledge of anatomy that the lay healers had at the time of the witch craze, could have been gained from the dead. If such women did gain their knowledge in this way, it is very unlikely that they would have made the source of their knowledge public. The Witchcraft Act of 1604 made grave robbing a capital offence. The Pendle Witches were reported as having interfered with corpses and feasted on dead babies (Bennett, 1957). The convicted woman, Janet Preston, is also said to have caused a corpse to bleed when she touched it (Lumby, 1995). In conclusion, the Pendle Witches' association with death could have been linked to healing, although it is difficult to be certain.

The growth of religious diversity during the Industrial Revolution

Whether or not the Pendle Witch Trials served the dual purpose of hunting out witches and warning Catholics, they certainly appeared to drive the practice even further under cover. By the time of the Industrial Revolution, the dominance of the established Protestant Church remained relatively unchallenged. In Bolton in the early 1800s, the Anglican Church was very influential and political. The Anglican clergy performed the duties of chaplains to the Freemasons, the Ancient Order of Druids, the Pitt Club and the Orangemen's Club. So great was the association between politics and religion that it was said that in Bolton, to be an Anglican was to be a Tory and to be a Dissenter was to be a Liberal. The Bolton Anglican Church at this time was also central to the life of the community and did much to alleviate the sufferings of the poor, despite the Protestant emphasis on self-help. The Church was also instrumental in improving the level of education of the poor and was concerned with this much more than 'brainwashing' the people into accepting the Protestant work ethic or religious doctrine. Sunday school records that have survived from the times, suggest that standards of teaching were in many ways superior to that offered in the state schools of today. And this was at a time when the state had shown little interest in education for the masses. Attempts were made to encourage critical as well as rote learning. When George Thistlewaite, curate of St George's wrote his own catechism in 1812, he asked that it be 'learned, not merely to be repeated, but to be understood' (Dale *op cit*). The development of the temperance movement led to practical and cultural contributions from religious groups as well. The Temperance Hall opened in 1840 on St George's Road, was one of the largest public meeting places in the town. The hall was a popular meeting place for political and religious groups who used it to hold a wide range of social events. The workers of the temperance movement believed in going out to meet the people, canvassing to attract followers in the streets. The musical marches of the early temperance workers led to the establishment of many of the brass bands we have in the North today. The prosperous Ashworth family of Eagley were devout Quakers who built modern mills, model villages, schools and shops. So, overall, most of the religious movements in Bolton made very positive contributions to the town.

A stricter form of the Protestant faith called Presbyterianism, began to emerge in Bolton in the mid 1600s. The Presbyterian faith is based on the teachings of John Calvin who preached a very strict moral code indeed. The influence of Presbyterianism in Bolton appears to have fluctuated over the years. There were three phases in the development of the faith. The first Presbyterian church was established in Bank Street, Bolton in 1696. The first patrons of the Church were the English Presbyterians, followed by the Scottish Presbyterians who flooded into the town during the 1800s. Strict Presbyterian teachings appear not to have been popular and Unitarian principles gradually replaced them. The third phase of Presbyterianism came with the establishment of St Andrews Church in 1937.[3] Oral accounts, from older women interviewed, suggest that Presbyterianism affiliation appears to have been much stronger during the 1930s and early 1940s. A Roman Catholic woman aged 85 years when interviewed, explained that she had married a Presbyterian. She said that the union could have caused trouble in many families. This is because there was a great deal of conflict between the Catholics and Presbyterians at the time (the woman had been married in the mid 1930s). However, in this case, the families of the bride and groom were friends so there was no serious conflict. Mild conflict did arise following the marriage, because of disagreements about which of the two should convert.

It seems that most Boltonians were quite religious during the nineteenth century. It is true that many employers put pressure on their workers to attend the church of their preference. Records from John Ainsworth's [4] 'Times and Wages Book' suggest that poor church attendance was usually caused by social problems, such as lack of appropriate clothing. Ainsworth's diary suggests that he did all he could to encourage church attendance in his workers. On March 18th 1848, for example, he wrote, 'I spoke to several of my workmen who had neglected to go to Church and desired that they

3   *Bolton Guardian*, 16th July, 1937.
4   John Horrocks Ainsworth owned the Bleach works on Halliwell Road, Bolton, established in 1739.

attend regular in future' (Cited in Dale, 1985). Ainsworth was by no means excessively paternal in his approach and appeared to respect the view of the 120 of his workers who expressed atheist beliefs quite openly.

The Industrial Revolution in the north led to a revival of the Catholic 'problem'. The rise in Catholicism in Bolton was partly, although not solely, due to the influx of Irish migrants into the town. This reached a peak during the 'Hungry Forties.' Prior to this period in 1767, a Catholic chapel was founded in Wood Street by John Shepherd. Shepherd quickly realised that anti-Catholic feeling in the area was very strong. He commented that 'a man dare scarcely proclaim himself a Roman Catholic in Bolton, so bitter was the popular sentiment against the principles of his church' (Dale, 1985). In 1800, St Peter and Paul's Church in Pilkington was founded. In the 1800s, there were large numbers of English as well as Irish Catholics in Bolton. The English, both Catholic and Protestant, believed the Irish to be a threat to the State. Although Dale stresses the amicability in which people of all denominations worked together in Bolton, racism and bigotry seem to have posed particular problems for the Irish throughout the nineteenth century. In the mid 1800s the Orange magistrates of Bolton collected a 10,000 named petition. The petition claimed that 'Catholics will become dangerous to the civil freedom of your Majesties subjects'. For all the bigotry they had to face, the Irish appeared to be quite capable of fighting back, at least in the literary sense of the [5] word. One of the co authors initially mistook the following for an example of anti-Catholic bigotry:

> *'Sir — To a certainty now, Mr Editor, is the acceptable time, now at last are the days of salvation now, when we are approaching the middle of the nineteenth century, is the fight of the Gospel, and true Christianity for the first time to dawn upon the Roman Catholics of this Empire and if all the angels rejoice at the conversation of one poor sinner, what will be the rejoicing of the celebration choir, when the millions of poor blinded papists (the worse of*

5   *Bolton Guardian*, 8th August, 1829.

*sinners) shall be converted from the error of their ways,
by the heaven depicted Captain Gordon and Mr John
Finch, assisted by the Rev John Wm Whittaker, Victor of
Blackburn. Let songs of praise and hallelujahs ascend
like incense to the God of Light, for thus sending amongst
us these singularly pious and enlightened men, to
illustrate our worse than Egyptian darkness, and to
rescue us from the whore of Babylon, the Pope and the
Devil. Tremble yea pillars of the Vatican for the
foundations of Catholicism are to be razed: the reformers
pigmy must now amount to colossal greatness and what
centuries of proscription and volumes of penal law have
failed to produce, vic — the total extinction of the Roman
Catholic Church'.*

Further reading however, revealed that the writer had been a
Catholic cynic commenting on the anti-Catholic climate of the
time. The writer continues:

*'The avowed object of these men is to convert all ages and
all nations to the 'Protestant Church'*

And with even further indignation:

*'Reform and convert the Catholics indeed! Let the
reformats first convert themselves — cleanse our streets
from the crowds of prostitutes at noon day, and then
begin with the Established Church where public and
monster evils exist and the God of purity, of justice and of
righteousness will bless and sanctify their labours'.*

The writer appears somewhat impatient with religious
disagreements which 'gloss' over what could be considered to
be the more important social issues of the time. The letter
concludes with a tone of defiance towards the Protestant
reformers. There is also a note of exasperation for the way the
Church appears to be ignoring social problems. The letter,
although probably exaggerating the evangelical spirit with
which religious reformers operate, has a practical tone. This
suggests that the writer may have felt the Church to be
somewhat out of touch with the day-to-day concerns of
ordinary people. Although written in 1829, a time when the
influence of religion was quite strong in the town, the letter is

interesting because it indicates some degree of distance between religion and the people. Dale notes that as the congregations of all denominations in the town became more middle-class, a distance between the Church and the working-classes began to emerge. The letter above supports this view. In it there is some implication of a growing division between the Church and the people. The increasing drift between the established church and ordinary people can be partly attributed to the delay in building sufficient numbers of new churches to cope with the rapidly growing population. Delays were caused because establishing a new church required the creation of a new parish. For the non-conformist religions no such problems existed. To found a chapel required only the right to occupy an appropriate building. Non-conformist religions that developed in Bolton during the industrial revolution include the Methodists, Unitarians and Quakers. The Unitarians were very respectable and conservative. Many were from affluent families with considerable political power in the town. One of the older women interviewed (aged 70 years) recalled a story one of the older men in her family had told her about the Quakers:

> *'The Quakers had a very practical kind of Christianity, they believed in doing. I remember one of my uncles telling me a story about one of the Quakers in Bolton. There was this young woman who had lost her husband and things could be very bad then, because there was no social security and she had a family. Well all the neighbours were round at the house and she was crying, 'what shall I do, what shall I do, how will I live?' And they were all saying how sorry they were. Well there was this Quaker in the group and he said 'well how sorry are you? Come on, lets see how sorry you are. And he went round there and then and got some money off them all and gave it to this woman.'*

The Methodist, John Wesley, was a frequent speaker in Bolton who drew large crowds each time he visited. The non-conformists, Methodists in particular, place less emphasis on buildings and more on the importance of faith in the heart. Many of the early Methodist meetings were held, not in chapels, but, in ordinary people's homes. The Mansions, a row of cottages in Doffcocker, Bolton provided one of these early meeting places. Here 'the men congregated on the ground floor, the women sat on the beds upstairs, the children sat in the attic, whilst such singers as there were sat on the stairs and led the whole assembly' (Dale, 1985). Trusties of the early Methodist chapels appear to have been mainly drawn from the working-class. Isaac Aspinal, for example, Trustee of a Methodist Chapel in Westhoughton, was a miner who worked in the pit with his wife. The faith of the Methodists in Bolton appears to have been very deep and must have offered great comfort in the event of a death. For example, the Bolton Methodist, Betty Bramwell, had spoken of God as her close friend whom she hoped one day to meet. Religious beliefs in Bolton, although diverse, appear to have been devout regardless of their affiliation. Newspaper reports, examined by one of the authors, suggest that belief in all denominations appears to have peaked during the First World War. At this time the funeral and memorial services held for the dead appear to have had quite spectacular attendance rates. This was not so noticeable during newspaper reports published during the Second World War. This observed difference was pointed out to one of the men interviewed (aged 70 years). The man replied that he could not be sure, but that he knew that the First World War appeared to have a greater impact on the people of Bolton. This was because of the high number of lives it claimed. Funerals during the war years appear to have been quite political as well as religious. We associate the union of Church and State with the past. However, the two appear to be reconciled during a war.

In order to continue this study, one of the writers has been conducting interviews with young people living in the Halliwell area. Halliwell is a working-class area of Bolton. This research is ongoing at the time of writing but the findings so far can be summarised in order to make an interesting conclusion to this chapter. Of the young people interviewed, none attend church on a regular basis. All expressed a belief in some form of life after death. Almost all of those interviewed had no clear idea of what form the afterlife might take. From these interviews, there appears to be an increase, among the young, of a belief in reincarnation. There was also a tendency for those interviewed to speak of life and death interchangeably. Clearly, ideas about life still shape ideas about death. The young people interviewed appear to have none of the Protestant work ethic of their forbears. Rather, they appear to enjoy 'being' rather than 'doing', living each day as it comes. Some, while talking of the meaning of life, made references to the relationship of humankind with nature. When asked about the type of funeral they preferred, almost all said that they preferred this to take the form of a celebration of the life of the deceased. A large percentage reported a preference for cremation rather than burial. In many respects, the young interviewed appeared to have a preference for the type of funeral favoured by many atheists. This was despite the fact that nearly all of those interviewed expressed a belief in God. Atheists and Humanists do not believe in an afterlife or in God. They prefer to celebrate human potential, experience and achievement in this life. In this respect, Humanists have ideas about life and death very similar to that of the Hebrews. To the early Hebrews, there was no individual life after death, but the individual lived on in the memories of the tribe (Pojman, 1992). The view is summarised in the New Testament: [6]

> *'For to him that is joined to all living there is no hope: for a living dog is better than a dead lion. For the living know that they shall die: but the dead know not anything, neither have they any more a reward: for the memory of them is forgotten. Also their love, and their hatred, and their envy, is now perished; neither have they any more a position for ever in anything that is under the sun. Go thy way, eat thy bread with joy, and drink thy wine with a merry heart; for God now accepteth thy works. Let thy garments always be white; and thy head lack no ointment. Live joyfully with the wife that Thou lovest all the days of the life of thy vanity, which he hath given thee under the sun, all the days of thy vanity: for that is thy portion in this life, and in thy life, and in thy labour*

6   *The Book of Ecclesiastes, Chapter 9.*

which Thou takest under the sun. Whatsoever thy hand
findeth to do, do it with thy might; for there is no works,
no device, nor knowledge, nor wisdom, in the grave,
whither Thou goest.'

So enjoy life now, its your only chance because there is nothing
beyond the grave. The position outlined in the bible forms the
foundation for the early secular slogan 'eat, drink and be
merry, for tomorrow we die.' This apparently light-hearted
view of life and death should not be mistaken as insincere, or
in any way disrespectful of life or indeed death. Secular
funerals can be very moving and usually involve some form of
celebration of the life of the deceased (Walter, 1997).

At the time of writing, the picture for the future of the
young seems quite depressing. A drug problem in the area has
led to a number of tragic deaths. There have also been some
accidental deaths. Unemployment for the youth of Halliwell is
high. Some of the young people interviewed have never had a
job. Yet all of the young people interviewed had an optimistic
view of life. In recent years, the Asian population of Bolton has
increased. Added to this increase has been a corresponding
growth in those subscribing to the Hindu and Muslin faiths.
What influence might all these changes might have on death
rituals? Mainly, when we examine the religious history of
Bolton, it has been the Christian faith that has dominated. As
we pointed out earlier in this chapter, when people of different
faiths live together, it is common for them adopt each others'
beliefs and practices. We are now living in a so-called Post
Modern world, which encourages the adoption of an eclectic
approach to most aspects of life. The interviews with young
westerners in Bolton suggest that certain commonalties are
beginning to emerge between East and West. These
commonalties include, a desire for some sense of affinity with
nature, a belief in reincarnation, a preference for cremation
and a value on 'being' rather than 'doing.' The future of
religious faith in Bolton is at the time of writing, speculative.
But it promises to be very interesting.

Chapter 3
Witchcraft and healing

The European witch craze began in the thirteenth century and ended around the mid eighteenth century, although it had not completely reached its conclusion even then. Feminist writers such as Ussher (1991) and Actherberg (1990) have argued that many of the women convicted of witchcraft during this period may have been lay healers. This chapter explores this argument, partly in relation to the Lancashire witches. The King of England, James I, was a strong believer in the existence of witchcraft. He commissioned the first translation of the Bible in which the phrase 'Thou shalt not suffer a witch to live' appeared. Reginald Scott objected to the meaning given to the Hebrew word 'Kashaph' because he belied that 'poisoner' was a more accurate interpretation than 'witch' but he was ignored (Achterberg, 1990). In 1597, King James published his 'Daemonologie' a text that was to become a bible for British witch hunters. A Lancashire woman called Alice Nutter, expressed her concern that 'the king's known superstitious dread of witches makes men seek them out to win his favour.' She also noted that, 'they have wonderfully increased since the publication of that baneful book!' (Ainsworth, 1995).[1] Thomas Potts was the Clerk of the Court at the Lancashire witch trials. Following the execution of the Lancashire witches, he published two pamphlets, 'The Arraignment and Triall of Jannet Preston, of Gisborne in Craven in the Countie of York' followed by 'The Wonderfull Discoverie of Witches in the Countie of Lancashire.' These pamphlets have provided historians with a descriptive account of the events that took place. However, interpretation of these sources needs to be cautious because of the writer's firm belief that the women were guilty.

---

1   Alice Nutter was one of the Lancashire women convicted during the Lancashire witch craze. The extract quoted is taken from Ainsworth's book which was a work of fiction based on fact.

New information has emerged in recent years suggesting that some of the women convicted of witchcraft, including the Lancashire witches, may have been lay healers. For example, Lumby (1995) argues it was Alizon Southern's innocent pride in the healing skills of her family that caused her to incriminate them when interviewed by the witch hunter, Roger Nowell. Alizon believed that Nowell's questions reflected a genuine interest in healing. Nowell interpreted Alizon's enthusiastic response to his questions as the basis of her confession. Alizon clearly believed that she was a witch who had possession of a power so great that even she was unable to control it. Alizon had argued with a peddler who later suffered a stroke and she took full responsibility for this.[2] Ehrenriech and English (1973) were two of the first feminist writers to suggest that the victims of the witch craze may have been healers. Since the publication of their pamphlet in the 1970s, other feminists have explored this argument. Some, such as Webb (1986) and Purkiss (1996), have been quite critical of the 'witch healer hypothesis' while others, such as Achterberg and Ussher consider that there may be some truth in it. Lumby's (1995) book on the Lancashire witches supports the argument and it is his book and the work of Achterberg which have provided the main sources for this chapter.

Lumby writes that some of the Lancashire witches, ie. Mother Chattox, had detailed knowledge of herbal remedies. These were probably no less effective than the purging and blood letting of the official medicine of the time. In Chapter 17 of his book, Lumby provides a fascinating analysis of some of the chants or spells used by the Lancashire witches. Many of the verses used by the witches may have been derived from Christian prayer.[3] At the execution of Jannet Preston, another of the Lancashire witches, there was a public outcry. Jannet protested her innocence to the end. Those who knew her well believed overwhelmingly that she had been 'taken away by practice'. Lumby, relates the meaning of the word 'practice' in

---

2   In the past people believed that witches could do both good and
     evil.
3'   At the time of the Lancashire witches prayer could be used to
     curse or charm.

this context, to the seventeenth century interpretation that means to plot or schemes. It is equally possible that the people referred to Jannet's healing practice.

Given the lack of unbiased information on the witch craze, it is difficult to be certain whether or not those convicted practised healing. It is probable that the witch craze came about because of a variety of factors. The activities of those who may have been healers has been lost to history because of the decree made by the Church and State that 'if a woman dare to heal without having studied, she is a witch and must die' (Michelet, 1862; cited by Ussher, 1991).The construction of new therories depends on plausible interpretations of the available information. Much of what has been written on the witch trials has been shaped by dualistic thinking. Distinctions, for example, have been made between white witches and black witches. This is inappropriate in the light of new evidence. We also have explanations for some of the reported activities of the witches, such as flying by night, informed by current western social science and medical theories. These have dismissed such reports as products of a deluded mind.

In some cases, such explanations may be quite valid. Certainly, some of the witches experienced flying and other similar states. But in the same way that many different elements may have constituted the rise of the witch craze, so, too, might a variety of issues lead to such reports or confessions (sometimes given spontaneously). However, the work of feminist writers such as Jeanne Achterberg, into women's history as healers, and shamanic practice provide possibilities for alternative explanations.

Many of the preparations used by the witch healers, such as belladonna, henbane and scopolamine, can produce altered states of consciousness and even death if taken in large doses. Reports of the behaviour of some of those convicted suggests that their mental state, at least when observed in custody, was 'unbalanced' to say the least.[4] For an account of

---

4   For an account of Alice Nutter's frame of mind while she was in
      custody the reader is referred to page 481 of on the Lancashire
      witches.

the hallucinatory state of Alice Nutter during her confinement, the reader is referred to *Page 481* of Ainsworth's book, 'The Lancashire Witches.'

When reading such accounts, it could be argued that these altered states of consciousness reflected psychotic illness as many writers have suggested. It could equally be argued that the tortures, food, drink and sleep deprivations inflicted by the inquisitors could have brought about such mental states. Equally, it could be argued that some of the women, knowing the torments they faced following arrest, attempted suicide by taking a lethal dose of one their (normally) healing preparations. They may well have been taking such preparations routinely and long before conviction because inducing altered states of consciousness is part of Shamanistic practice.

The Shamanic approach to healing exists in many societies, and is particularly prevalent in eastern cultures. It was probably the dominant approach to healing in the west prior to the introduction of Christianity. Shamanic practice is 'holistic,' concerned with the health of mind, body and spirit. This concern includes, not only the needs of the person requiring care, but to the healer as well. In the truest sense, the healer and the sick are involved in a relationship from the start. Spirituality is fundamental to Shamanic practice, so that strategies for inducing altered states of consciousness during the healing process, particularly in relation to pain control, are quite common. Such strategies may involve the use of drugs or rituals, such as chanting. In recent years chanting has proved to be a very effective method of pain control, particularly during childbirth.

The practice of Shamanism is closer to nature than contemporary western medicine. Shamans in many cultures draw on the spiritual power, present in nature, of animal spirits, such as eagles, wolves and, of course, cats. Mother Chattox loved animals and kept quite a few pets. Chattox made images of her animal companions but whether or not this activity was part of her 'magic' is unknown. Nonetheless, it was used as evidence to convict her. Witches were believed to have animal 'familiars', usually cats. In some towns, sacks of live cats were burned with their owners. Given that cats are the natural enemies of plague-carrying rats, this must have increased the prevalence of the disease (Achterberg, 1990).

Another characteristic of the religious aspect of Shamanism, is that good and evil are contained in one deity or persona. Within this conceptual framework, it is inappropriate to speak of black and white witches as separate individuals, since the same individual would be capable of cursing and curing. This understanding helps to explain one of the contradictions faced by those who condemned the witches. In the early years of the witch trials, lay people opposed the prosecution of white witches because of the services they provided to the community (Scarre, 1987). The problem was that many of those convicted of witchcraft appeared to do both good and evil. Therefore, the witch hunters had problems distinguishing between a black and a white witch. Given the thousands of men and women who were convicted and executed, this was clearly a minor deterrent.

In ancient times and indeed, well into the years of the Enlightenment, healers in the west delivered a general, as opposed to a specialised, practice. In the recent past, for example, community midwives delivered babies in the labouring mother's home. Following the delivery, the midwife would stay in the home of the newly delivered mother for a few days, until she had recovered her strength (Ehrenriech and English, 1973). The midwife had several female attendants helping her, who provided collective and holistic care for the new mother and her child (Purkiss, 1996). Similarly, lay healers cared for the sick and, in the event of a death, took care of the corpse, as well as offering practical and emotional support for the bereaved. Reports of such practices suggest that this was typical in many working-class communities well into the 1940s.

Rituals, such as washing the corpse, the connections between femininity and women's perceived affinity with the elements, such as fire and water, influenced death rituals, long after nursing became a profession. It is helpful to trace the history of lay healers and the way that their practice faded following the Enlightenment, because this allows us to develop connections between past and present. This chapter continues with a brief discussion of the history of lay healers in Ancient and early Christian times. We will discuss the gradual exclusion of women from healing practice in relation to:

- how the development of the male-dominated medical profession may have influenced this exclusion

and

- how this may have contributed towards the rise of the witch craze.

Before the development of dualistic thinking in the west, people perceived the world very differently. Close connections existed between life and death. It was rare for people to hide illness and death (and even corpses) from public view. Indeed, in sixteenth century Paris, in the Cemetery of the Innocents, described by Aries (1974), corpses rested in open graves. Human remains, including bone, were frequently used as decoration by the living:

> *'Above these galleries were the ossuaries in which skulls and limbs were artistically arranged. This striving after artistic effects with bones — a form of decoration which was both baroque and macabre — ended in the mid 18th century.'*

In an environment where there was little fear or revulsion for the dead, witches and magicians practised quite openly. Successful magical practice invariably included rituals associated with death. Exactly what these practices were, it is difficult to say, since most references to them are rather vague. The dominant assumption, at the time of the witch trials, was that these activities with the dead were evidence of evil. James I passed a statute condemning to death anyone found 'taking up dead bodies from their graves to be used in any witchcraft.' In more recent years, the Reverend Montague Summers, a twentieth century advocate of the continued existence of witches, wrote of the Roman Etruscans:

> *'Etruscan divines foretold future events from the inspection of the warm and palpating entrails of victims, sometimes animals, sometimes human, and these horrid sacrifices were clandestinely offered in Rome itself, especially under the Emperors.'*

Summers also wrote of evil 'dwellers amongst tombs' (ie. healers) who, like the Etruscans, sought knowledge from the dead. The witches were also accused of meeting in cemeteries, in or around tombs. Some of the witches were reported to have dug up the dead and to have interfered with them in order to gain knowledge. The accusers referred to knowledge of the occult in this context but the witches could have been seeking knowledge of anatomy from the dead. In *Chapter 8*, we discuss the resurrectionists, people who stole corpses which they sold to anatomists. It may be that the witches were also early anatomists. It is now considered quite respectable to learn anatomy and physiology from the dissection of corpses. Using knowledge gained from such sources, today's doctors, foretell future events, just as the Etruscans did.

Doctors give patients a prognosis, ie. they tell patients what the expected outcome of their illness is likely to be, based on the doctor's knowledge of anatomy, physiology and disease processes. Harvesting the dead to conduct transplant surgery is also common practice. It is clear from the reports that some of those accused of witchcraft had a basic knowledge of anatomy and physiology. Purkiss, for example, writes:

> *'A Northumbrian woman called Margaret Stothard was summoned when Jane Carr's child was suffering from a terrible illness believed to be caused by witchcraft. Stothard cured the child by putting her mouth into the child's mouth, whereupon 'she made much chirping and sucking.' After this magical mouth to mouth resuscitation, she said she 'would warrant the child would do well enough'*

> (Purkiss, 1996).

The witches and their associates were also accused of eating and making ointment from the flesh of dead infants. Reports about these acts of cannibalism do not refer specifically to which parts of the dead baby were eaten. However, it could have been the placenta? Eating the placenta is beneficial for a newly delivered mother because this can replace important nutrients lost during delivery. It is for this reason that newly delivered mothers are encouraged to eat the placenta in some parts of New Guinea. Given the scale of poverty that existed at the time of the witch crazes, it may have been wise to encourage a newly delivered mother to eat her placenta.

Ointments made from the flesh of dead infants were supposedly used by the witches to cast spells, heal and to help in conducting their occult affairs. It was believed that the ointments helped the witches to fly and, when used as a lubricant, gain access to houses by slithering down chimneys (Trevor-Roper, 1969). Plainly, the flesh of dead babies was believed to be source of supernatural power. At the time of the witch craze, there was a belief that babies, whether alive or dead, had a spiritual potency that could help in the process of healing. For example, Prukiss writes of a midwife called Mistress Pepper who healed the sick by placing an infant in the sickbed, face to face with the invalid. Pepper believed that infants had the power to 'suck' out the evil spirit that was making the invalid ill. In the West Indies, there is a common belief that the spirit of a dead baby is more powerful than that of a dead adult. Drawing on the spiritual power of animals is another characteristic of the Shaman's practice. In parts of Africa where Voodoo is still practised, the flesh of dogs is used as a base for many ointments.[5] This may be due to a belief that the spiritual power of the animal will add to the potency of the ointment. In the west, there was once a belief that the snake possessed a healing power that could be exploited by healers. We now use patches rather than oral preparations to administer certain drugs because these are more effective when absorbed through the skin. Putting these facts together, it seems that many of the witches' activities with the dead were not as bizarre as they first appear. This is particularly relevant if we fit the practices of the witches into a Shamanic framework.

In conclusion, we return to the question of whether some of the witches could have been healers. Given the reports of their visits to tombs and cemeteries, and their advanced knowledge of anatomy, it seems reasonable to suppose that they may well have been. Prior to the witch craze, it was quite

5   Thanks to Paul Amuna of South Bank University for this
     information.

acceptable for people to consult a witch or wizard for help. People would consult them for cures, advice on the future, and even to rid their houses of rats and mice (Scarre, 1987). We now know that it is necessary to exercise caution before we dismiss faith in the supernatural as little more than ignorance. Lay healers once presented themselves as witches or magicians. Many had detailed knowledge of muscles, bones, herbs and a variety of other healing sources and practices, such as resetting dislocated bones (Ehrenriech and English, 1973).

When we examine the 'magic' of these early healers, we find that this art was clearly more 'scientific' than the 'science' of the early medical men. The witch healers based their practice on empiricism, a systematic observation of cause and effect. They were very close to nature, the seasons, the universe and the flesh. The Church had established a belief that all of these were evil by the end of the Middle Ages. Scientists, such as Bacon who emphasised the importance of learning from nature, did not distinguish between science and magic.

Scarre considers that this approach to scientific discovery may have originated from Neoplatonic thinking. This was a scientific perspective that embraced ideas about certain forms of high magic. There was a belief that knowledge of magic would allow humankind to harness the forces of nature and use them to benefit humanity. Such an understanding of 'magic' is almost identical to what we now consider to be scientific rational thinking. This approach preceded the development of dualistic thinking and it was more holistic. Scarre, describes this perceived unity between magic and nature as follows:

> *'Just as plucking one taut string of a lyre will cause a second string to vibrate in sympathy with it, so are all parts of the universe linked together in a single harmonious rhythm which enables the magician who performs the correct actions to capture and use the powers of the heavenly bodies.'*

Ideas such as those expressed in the above quotation, do not appear to be in any way evil or corrupt. But, in the thirteenth century, people could be burned alive for expressing such sentiments? Having come full circle, in that science is now about the observation of nature, we have still managed to retain the legacy of dualistic thinking?

At the present time, nurses (usually women) are subordinate to doctors (usually men) who dominate western ideas about health, illness and cure. So, unlike the early healers who, as we have noted, combined care and cure in one practice, we have a division. Writers such as Achterberg (1990) argue that in pagan prehistoric cultures, healers were usually female. These women enjoyed respect and held high status in the communities that they served. Their practice reflected a close affinity with nature and the early pagan religions, many of which worshipped female and male gods. The pagan gods were believed to be capable of acts of good and evil. How and why women's position changed is open to speculation. Meanwhile, we turn to a discussion of how ideas about witchcraft may have influenced death rituals.

Chapter 4
Witchcraft, fire and water
and the rites of passage:

Chapter 3 examined the theory that some of the Lancaster witches may have been healers. This chapter discusses how the legacy of the witch may have influenced death rituals, in particular the laying out process. Ehrenriech and English (1973) write that:

> *'The witch hunts left a lasting effect. An aspect of the female has ever since been associated with the witch, and an aura of contamination has remained — especially around the midwife and other women healers.'*

Whether or not women enjoyed any credibility as healers prior to the witch craze, they were left with very little following its conclusion. Nevertheless, lay or informal healers continued their holistic practice, at least in the north of England, well into the present century. Their role and identity as healers blurred into the role of wife and mother. Many working-class communities benefited substantially from the care these women provided. Although an aspect of the feminine did remain in their practice, it did not always do so in the negative way described by Ehrenreich and English. The layer-out is discussed in greater detail in *Chapter 7*. In this chapter we consider how the practice of the layer-out, and indeed many professional nurses, retain some associations with pagan religion and witchcraft.

The layer-out was a woman who made a living, during the nineteenth century, washing and preparing the corpse shortly after a death. These were carers who had not completed any formal nursing training. Despite the lack of formal qualifications, there were striking similarities between the procedures of the layer-out and those used by 'professional' nurses. One example is the practice of leaving the body for an hour after death to give the soul sufficient time to leave the corpse. Autobiographic accounts, such as Brittain's 'Testament of Youth' (1933) suggests further evidence of the ritual and spiritual overtones in the laying-out process. Another ritual that held great symbolic meaning was the washing of the corpse.

The practice of washing the corpse has deep spiritual meaning in many cultures and is surrounded by taboos and regulations. One of the authors, a former nurse, remembers that the corpse would be washed regardless of whether or not this was necessary on the grounds of cleanliness. Sometimes the deceased had been washed shortly before death occurred. During her time as a nurse, the author did on one occasion, challenged this practice. A patient had died in the ward and the author asked her colleagues if washing the deceased was necessary. The deceased had been bed bathed only a few hours prior to the death. The author's colleagues responded to the query with some hostility. They insisted that the corpse should be washed as a token of respect.

The author did not challenge her colleagues any further because, basically, she agreed with them. She had questioned the practice because she had started to think about the symbolic meaning of the washing rather than the practicalities of it. From the author's point of view, her agreement with the ritual of washing the dead may stem from her Catholic origins. In the Catholic church, water is perceived to have spiritual and purifying properties. Water is used for baptism and holy water is sprinkled on the coffin during the requiem mass. The anthropologist, Brendann (1930), who has conducted research into cross cultural variations in death rituals, asks us to consider that:

> 'here we might call attention to the enormous role played by water in religious ceremonies for we well know its use is by no means confined to the death situation. In the history of many peoples, although water has its nymphs, nexen and its purifying gods, yet it is water that always remains sacred, divine, mighty. The immediate valuations of the elements finds expression in the Persian religion, where the practical use of water is connected with its worship. Water is kept 'pure' first because of its divine character and then because of it's 'human' character, and what is more important, its human

character survives even after the divine has been eliminated. '

(Brendann, 1930)

Roberts has commented on the similarities in the practices of the care provided for the young, the old and the dead. These procedures had spiritual and sexual overtones expressed by the ritual of washing and the symbolism of water. Such symbolic overtones are eloquently discussed by Brittain:

'Towards the men I came to feel an almost adoring gratitude for their simple and natural acceptance of my ministrations. Short of actually going to bed with them, there was hardly any intimate service that I did not perform for one or another in the course of four years, and I still have some reason to be thankful for the knowledge of masculine functioning which the care of them gave me, and for the my earliest release from the sexual inhibitions that even today — thanks to the Victorian tradition which up to 1914 dictated that a young woman should know nothing of men but their faces and their clothes until marriage pitch-forked her into an incompletely visualised and highly disconcerting intimacy — beset many of my contemporaries, both married and single. In the early days of the war, the majority of soldier patients belonged to a first rate physical type, which neither wounds nor sickness, unless mortal, could permanently impair and from the constant handling of their lean, muscular bodies I came to understand the essential cleanness, the innate nobility of sexual love.'

(Brittain, 1933)

Brittain wrote that, following the war, many nurses suffered discrimination because they were considered 'loose.' This illustrates some of the contradictions we live with but do not consider in any real depth. Social rules, prejudices and beliefs associate women, femininity and sexuality with all that is good, wholesome and pure. In direct contradiction, these perceptions are also associated with all that is wild, immoral and dirty.

Such contradictions also exist in relation to sickness, death and the corpse. On the one hand, there is fear, disgust and revulsion, while, on the other, there is a recognition and respect for the dignity of the corpse because it symbolises a human being. This is why basic caring procedures, such as bed bathing and laying-out, are in essence, rituals of care — rituals of love. Water is an important means by which the symbolism implicit in such rituals is conveyed. In the eighteenth century, there was a common belief that the healing process could be accelerated by washing a sick person's clothes in running water and drying them out in the sun (Purkiss, 1996). This is another example of how people have drawn on the powers of the earth elements (fire and water) in order to aid the healing process and to protect the sick. Washing and drying cloths are feminine activities in most cultures and symbolise the safety of the home as a, mainly woman's, sanctuary from the harsh realities of the external world.

Water symbolises the rites of passage. In Freud's 'Interpretation for Dreams' water symbolises amniotic fluid. In his lecture on Symbolism, Freud suggested that:

> *'Birth is almost invariably represented by something which has connection with water: one either falls into the water, or drinks out of it, one rescues someone from the water or is rescued by someone — that is to say, the relationship is one of mother to child.'*

(Freud, 1973)

Rycroft (1979) notes that dreams of birth are also dreams of, a possibly longed for, rebirth.

Chapter 3 discussed how many cultures associate femininity with nature, the earth and its elements, such as fire and water, spirituality, emotionality and holism. Culturally, women are considered to have a closer affinity with nature than men. Some people, even today, believe that women's behaviour is determined by their biology and sexuality because of their ability to give birth to and nourish an infant. Freud (1973) considered that the mind had a habit of exploring such contradictions in dreams. Freud believed that the female body is typically represented in dreams as a landscape, with rocks, woods and water. He wrote that 'The range of things which are given symbolic representation in dreams is not wide: the human body as a whole.' Of the female body, Freud wrote that 'some symbols have more connection with the uterus than the female genitals.' Freud considered that various containers, such as cupboards, stoves and rooms were symbolic of the female body. When we consider witchcraft, the image of the stove is quite potent. The stove can be used to nurture, by helping someone to provide food. Or, as in many children's tales, the stove can be used to 'cook', 'burn' or 'choke to death.'

Purkiss has shown how ideas about witchcraft may be associated with loathing and longing for the maternal body[1] that is a safe haven and a source of pollution. She notes the association made in many cultures between the observed fluidity and 'leakyness' of the female body and ideas about maternity and witchcraft. This perceived fluidity formed the basis of the belief that witches could transform their shape. Aristotle considered women's bodily fluidity a serious problem. In order that this fluidity did not cause women to disintegrate into a 'mush', they needed to have sexual intercourse with men. Men's sperm, according to Aristotle, warmed the female body and, having a similar action to rennet, allowed it to maintain some solidity. Water and fluidity are associated with stages in the life cycle, including birth (or pre-birth) and death. Purkiss points out that popular images of the witch represent different stages of a woman's life — the maid, the earth mother and the old hag.

Anthony writes that in some cultures, cerebrospinal fluid and seminal fluid are associated with moisture and dryness which are both important in the transition of the psyche through different stages of existence. Burning the corpse liberates the psyche so that it can join the spirits while the bones retain the genesis and potency of the dead in the same way that a seed retains the fertility of the plant. The seed has to be dried before it is sown for the purpose of germination and for rebirth it requires dampness. This is why pouring a

---

1   This refers to the body of the mother as general and symbolic and
     does not relate to the real body of a real woman.

liquidation is considered in many cultures to be a sign of hope for the dead. In the process described, there is no separation of humankind from nature. Instead humankind is part of the cycle of nature.

Some individuals, including many academics, believe in a lost civilisation that existed in prehistoric times. This civilisation was matriarchal and ruled by a deity called the 'Great Goddess' or 'Great Mother.' Freud made references to the ways this lost matriarchy might be represented in dreams. He linked the lost civilisation with the feminine mind which he considered unknowable — 'the Dark Continent.' Relating this to the Lancashire witches, it seems that Potts had similar ideas. He referred to Lancashire as a vast area and a suitable habitat for witches. This demonstrates some of the problems that can arise when concepts are associated with beliefs in a lost continent or civilisation dominated by women. This reinforces the notion that women are controlled by their hormones, their biology, with savagery and evil.

The psychologist, Jung, developed Freud's ideas about dreams, witchcraft and great goddesses even further. According to Jung, knowledge of prehistoric cultures are stored in the furthest corners of our minds in a location Jung referred to as the collective unconscious (Jacobi, 1975). The maternal body of this goddess represented the earth (as discussed in *Chapter 2*) and is related to the human mortal body, ie. we come from, and return to, dust. Some feminists associate the symbol of fire and the pain of burning with salvation from the constraints of a patriarchal society. An alternative to the oppressive nature of patriarchy is offered in the image of the Cosmic Mother. This was a goddess who flew around the universe with milk dripping from her breasts. Droplets of this milk formed the embryos of new stars. A more direct association with witchcraft, water and death is made by Starhawk (1979). According to her the beginning of witchcraft was a time when:

> *'Life and death were a continuous stream; in lowland pools, reindeer does, their bellies filled with stones that embodied the souls of deer, were submerged in the waters of the mother's womb, so that victims of the hunt could be reborn.'*

Others have queried whether the lost city of Atlantis might have been the lost civilisation. Atlantis was a city submerged under the sea. Mermaids are a type of witch whose domain is the sea rather than the earth. We do not hear of mermaids in fresh water. Sea water is denser and saltier, and a body floats more easily than in freshwater. Thus, sea water has more similarity to amniotic fluid than does freshwater. Love stories of humans and mermaids may represent a kind of death wish, a desire to return to the safety of the womb.

Jung (1982) also believed that shadows of prehistoric civilisations were represented in dreams and, so too, were the masculine and femine dimensions of our personality. When men dream of a witch or Great Goddess, this symbolises the feminine side of their personality. The death rituals that may have been influenced by ideas, such as those discussed above, are based on the notion of an after life and the rites of passage. Women's role in procedures, such as laying-out, may have developed as extensions of women's caring role, into the after life of the dead person. As part of the nurturing process, this role would include provision of comforts and refreshments. Here again, water is important, and not only for washing. Another common belief across cultures is the belief in the existence of a thirsty ghost. The tribes of Herbert River leave food and drink near the graves of their dead for the ghosts to drink, as do high cast Hindus, the people of the Kutaba tribe of Australia and the natives of Maranoa. An equally common belief is that ghosts cannot cross water and the people of some cultures spill water along the route of the funeral procession so that the ghost will be unable to come back to annoy the living (Brendann, 1930).

In recent times, women, sexuality and reproduction have been closely related to the theme of death. The connection has been more explicitly recognised, and even celebrated, in pagan religions. To an extent, such connections may have been based on pragmatic principles because in the past many women died in childbirth. Other writers have commented on the similarity between sexual excitement and dangerous, life threatening situations (Kastenbaum, 1988; Baldwinson, 1996). The link between sexuality and death may have also come about because of sexually transmitted diseases. In Kastenbaum's words:

'Romantic intimacy, sexual relations and procreation were all threatened by a disease that might not only take one's life, but also stain one's reputation.'

Sexuality and the life-cycle are also linked to the contradiction of the good and the bad maternal body. The 'bad' maternal body leaks fluids and can leave stains behind, just as a stigmatising disease can leave a 'stained' memory of the deceased in the minds of the living. Thus, fear of death may be linked to fear of the maternal body. Women's participation in death rituals varies across cultures. In those cultures where women wash and prepare the corpse, it is usually the men who take the body to the cemetery or crematorium. So the role of men and women is not challenged in the event of a death. Women provide 'care' of the corpse by the rituals of washing and presenting the corpse. They do this traditionally in the house — the symbol in dreams of maternity. Men then take the corpse to begin its unknown journey into death. Freud also wrote that dying is represented in dreams by departure, often by a train journey. When women finish the job of nurturing, it is the role of men to sever the maternal link so that the person cared for can go out into the world.

The distinction between the home, the family and the mother has always been significant in English culture. In the past, giving birth and nursing an infant during the first few days of life was seen as a very sensitive time. In some parts of the country, men would be excluded from the house as soon a woman began labour. The labouring woman would be attended by a midwife, her mother and a group of female attendants called 'gossips'. During labour and following delivery, the latch on the door of the house would be kept on. The mother, the midwife and her attendants would share a drink made from warm ale, herbs and spices. The drink was supposed to have medicinal properties but, in sharing it, the women demonstrated their solidarity and concern for the mother and child. Following the delivery, the mother would have to stay in the house during the lying-in period until she was considered fit enough to go to Church for purification. Her re-entry into the public domain of the village was loaded with symbolic meaning and was referred to as 'letting off the latch' (Purkiss, 1996).

As a child grows, mothers are supposed to provide a safe base in the home for the child and, indeed, for the rest of the family. As Purkiss notes, the good woman 'keeps house.' However, the mother is also supposed to know the appropriate time to 'let go' of the child, when he or she is ready to live an independent life. The 'smother mother' refers to the stereotype of the mother who will not allow her children to go into the world to live an independent, adult life. Now this is problematic for several reasons. For a mother to strike the right balance of encouraging independence without being accused of neglecting the child is difficult. This is not made easier when the limits on the age at which an individual can be regarded as an adult vary across time and cultures. However, the time will come when the child goes into the world, leaving the mother behind in the home.

These similarities to concepts of child development, and the role of the home and the mother in it, are interesting when compared with the laying-out process. This suggests that death rituals are used to mimic the normal patterns of life, thus making death more acceptable. These similarities may not be considered at a conscious or even individual level. The motivation or basis for these practices may be so deeply buried in the collective unconscious that they will never be fully understood. But they are points to explore from a religious and theoretical perspective. It is interesting to note that religions based on witchcraft and paganism still exists and, indeed, appear to be growing. Many witches at the present time prefer to practice their religion in secret due to the harassment they still attract. Witch and pagan religions are essentially religions of fertility, nature and the cycle of life (Purkiss, 1996).

Chapter 5
The informal carer: Care of the sick and dying from the 1800s to the present time

By the mid 1700s, belief in witchcraft had declined and there were very few witch trials after this time. By the nineteenth century, science and medicine had become the established authorities on all matters relating to health, illness and death. Scientific rationality, at least in the conventional sense, had eliminated the mystique and the spiritual from the deathbed scene. Religious bodies had surrendered responsibility for the care of the dying, from the priest to the physician. The context of death moved from the death bed at home to the hospital ward (Houlbrooke, 1989).

Information on informal women healers following the witch craze is very limited. In the case of the witches, there is some evidence, even if it was provided by their persecutors. Although biased, this provides a starting point for an analysis. The history of women as informal carers is even more limited than that on witches and healers and source data for this chapter has been difficult to find.

From the mid eighteenth century, the history of women as carers and healers has been submerged in the history of professional nursing. This has led to an over simplification of facts. The history of the professional nurse differs from that of lay healers in a variety of ways. It is understandable that the history of each becomes confused because each provided the warp and weft of, what came to be, a singular cloth — the nursing profession. The nursing profession has changed dramatically during the last twenty years. Its history is interesting, but we feel that the informal carer also deserves an autonomous history, because the story of nursing is mainly middle-class. To equate the story of healthcare always with nursing denies yet another group of working-class people a place in history. Even if remembered, the history of informal caring risks being represented in a biased way if it is recorded only in traditional nursing texts. This has already happened. In many traditional nursing history books, the story of the informal carer has been generally negative (Kenny, 1992).

This chapter and *Chapter 3* attempts to redress the balance, at least in relation to death and dying. Due to the difficulties in locating information, we have drawn almost entirely on oral accounts gathered by one of the authors to write this section. To develop our discussion we have also drawn on secondary sources, most notably the work of Adams and Roberts who have conducted similar work. Ehrenreich and English (1973) write that the evolution of nursing led to a relatively new perspective on the history of women as healers. They are quite critical of nursing arguing that, as a profession, it has done little to empower women by affording them an equal status with men. They also argue that nursing perpetuates rather than challenges inequitable gender relationships. Middle-class women invented professional nursing during the nineteenth century in order to provide an occupation for themselves and a respectable alternative to marriage.

We acknowledge that many professional nurses at the present time do not fit this stereotype. We have already acknowledged that nursing has changed during the last few years and also that it attracts people from diverse backgrounds. In this book we are writing about the historical roots of nursing rather than its contemporary state or practice.[1] When we consider the nursing histories so far constructed, it is important to consider that the middle-class women of the Nightingale school, had a vested interest in presenting informal carers in negative ways. Thus, discussions of the informal carer in numerous official nursing reports since the turn of this century need to be interpreted with some caution (Kenny, 1992; 1993).

Most conventional texts on nursing history refer to untrained women who worked in the hospitals. The nursing care delivered in most nineteenth century hospitals was appalling and provided by a motley, drunken and unsavoury

---

1   In many ways, however, contemporary nursing is still influenced by the Nightingale legacy.

type of person — the rejects and dropouts of society. But conditions in the hospitals were also appalling. Many of these institutions had been established in the eighteenth century and were based, initially, on humanitarian principles. By the end of this era, they had become little more than refuges for the poor, sick, dying and pauper lunatics (Scull, 1996). A committee set up to investigate conditions at the Bellevue Hospital in New York during the 1870s reported that not a single bar of soap was found on the premises. Funding was provided for only the very basics and for the minimum of care (Ehrenreich and English, 1973). The inadequate diets provided in some asylums amounted to a policy of semi starvation that led to a sharp increase in patient mortality rates around the early 1900s. Such institutions were hardly likely to attract the services of anyone who had more favourable alternatives in life, such as providing informal care in a community setting. Care in the community, past and present poses further methodological problems. Many families, even at the present time, care for sick or infirm family members. To read many of the transcripts of data collected for this book, there is very little difference in the stories of informal caring given by young or older interviewees. The only noticeable difference between the two groups was the isolation reported by younger carers in comparison with the older women who spoke of shared networks of care.

The Athlone Report (1939) was the earliest official survey published on the activities of the untrained carer in hospitals. On the whole the report commended the contribution made by these carers. But the report also expressed concern that the untrained carer posed a threat to the professional nurse. The solution to the problem was to develop the skills of the untrained women so that they served as 'handy women' to the, mainly middle-class, State Registered Nurses. These early handy women provided the prototype for yesterday's State Enrolled Nurse and today's NVQ trained support workers (Kenny, 1992). The history of the untrained women who provided care in hospitals and their relationship to the professional nurse who supervised her, is documented in traditional nursing history books. Informal carers in the community appear to have remained fairly autonomous for much longer than their hospital-based counterparts. Unfortunately, the informal community carers lacked formal education and given their busy lifestyle, few had time for writing. It is only in recent years that the professional nurse has switched the focus of her practice from the hospital into the community. Due to these and other factors, the story of the informal community carer has been for the most part lost to history.

That the role of informal carers appears to have been unclear, adds even further to the difficulties encountered in attempts to construct their history. Some informal carers were generic in their practice while others specialised in one area, such as midwifery. For this reason, the writers make the point that when we refer to the informal carer and the layer-out, in many instances we could be referring to the same person. In addition, there is lack of clarity and consistency in the informal carers and layer-outs' relationships to the families and communities they served. The work of Roberts (1989) and Adams (1993) suggest that, in the past, informal carers were employed from outside the family circle. However, data collected for this book, from both oral and archive sources, suggests the that the role of informal caring and laying-out was integrated into the overall responsibilities of homemakers and mothers.

Whether in the home or in the community, informal carers in the past did not work in isolation. Informal networks of care and co-operation in the working-class communities of the time developed out of necessity more than anything else, because working-class people could not afford to pay for professional care. Attempts to gather some archive material on informal carers, proved to be relatively unsuccessful. Newspapers examined from the 1800s yielded only two references to informal carers and one reference to a layer-out. A report of the 1832 cholera outbreak referred to a mother who developed symptoms and then died after caring for family members.[2] Another article on the cholera outbreak did make

2   *Bolton Chronicle*, 1st September, 1832.

reference to female caring attendants but did not present them in a very good light.[3] According to the report:

> 'A poor unfortunate lad had been suddenly seized with an attack of the cholera of so malignant a nature, that he was deprived of speech and motion, instantaneously and that the only sign of life was an occasional violent convulsion. These primary symptoms of the case were not corresponding with those which the old women by whom he was attended had read, it was presumed that that the secondary symptoms had seized him first. Messages were sent off in every direction for medical aid and also to convey the mournful intelligence to his friends. In the interval which elapsed prior to the surgeon's arrival, the poor victim had been attended to by as many persons who could possibly thrust themselves into the room to which he had been conveyed, and he was supplied with brandy, gin and other stimulating liquors in such plentiful proportions, with a view to create circulation that they at length succeeded. The functions of the stomach were brought into action and as tremendous stretching followed as it was possible to conceive, in fact it appeared quite satisfactory to his attendants who declared with evident pleasure who declared that they had now brought the disorder round and again supplied the unfortunate wretch with more brandy.'

The report continues to describe the arrival of the surgeon, who bled the young man, after which the former noted that 'violent convulsions had been replaced by violent hiccups'. The surgeon questioned the patient and found that the latter had been drinking alcohol since the early hours of that morning. By midday the patient had become so drunk that he collapsed and observers assumed that he was suffering from an attack of the cholera. The surgeon recorded a diagnosis of intoxication.

The report, if taken at 'face value', suggests that the women who cared for the young man were very ignorant. But before drawing such conclusions, a number of points need to

3   *Bolton Chronicle*, 15th September, 1832.

be considered. The first is that during the 1800s most people drank alcohol quite frequently because it was cheaper than coffee or tea and cleaner than water from the public taps. In the 1800s, the smell of alcohol on most people, including children would be considered quite normal. Secondly, we need to consider that the 1832 outbreak of cholera had claimed several deaths prior to the man presenting symptoms.

The cholera had caused a panic in the town and it is understandable that, when presented with a person in a state of collapse, the women attendants would immediately think of cholera. In the 1800s, drunks were common — collapsed drunks were not. The report refers to the fact that the women had read about the symptoms of cholera. That the attendants were able to read and understand medical texts is quite significant when we consider the events discussed took place in the early 1800s.

Information from John Ainsworth's 'Time and Wages Book'[4] reveals that of 321 workers, 227 could read and write leaving 94 who could not. So at the time there was still quite a large proportion of the town's population who could not read. The women referred to could not only read and write, they could understand medical texts.[5] The women misdiagnosed the symptoms they observed on the occasion discussed, but this becomes understandable if we consider the circumstances. Reconsidering the report, it seems unfortunate that the women were referred to as ignorant. The social context of all information should be considered in order to avoid misinterpretations.

Another point worthy of note is that the women came to the man's aid immediately without guarantees of financial reward for the care they provided. The older Bolton women interviewed did not distinguish between informal carers and professional nurses. They referred to both as 'nurses'. The late maternal great grandmother of one of the authors had

4   This information was collected by Ainsworth between 1800 and 1845 and is reproduced in Dale (1985).

5   It is accepted that we do not know the source from which the women obtained their information. However, the point made is that the women had tried to improve their knowledge by reading around the topic.

been a midwife. The author asked her late grandmother whether the great grandmother had received any formal training. The reply given was that the great grandmother had indeed received training — from other midwives of the community. Attempts during the interviews to clarify to whom the older women were referring when they spoke of 'the nurse', yielded similar responses, 'Why it was other nurses who trained them.' The author failed to establish whether her interviewees were referring to formal or informal training. The point is that most of the older Bolton women seemed unconcerned as to the type of training the 'nurse' had received. What mattered was the 'nurse's' ability to care.

Caring for the sick is a skilled practice and readers may be concerned by the older women's failure to be impressed by formal qualifications. However, it is important not to be too dismissive about the skills of the informal carer. From the information gathered, it appears that many were excellent 'nurses' who used what one might call 'natural' remedies to tend the sick. Some of these remedies are noted in the poem presented below:

Remedies

> If you complained of feeling sick,
> Soda Bicarbonate soon did the trick
> It made you want to spew up more
> But you'd end up thrown out the door.

> They'd say "You're better in fresh air
> Now off to school and do take care"
> To keep your constitution ticking
> Syrup of figs would take some licking.

> Or maybe, in more stubborn case,
> Castor oil you'd have to face.
> But woe betide, if you copped a wound,
> with Friars Balsam's fire made you fly round the room.

> Dettol, for hygiene, in the tin bath
> You'd change to bright red, in the aftermath.
> Barley, for kidneys, improving their works
> Durbac, for hair, if nasties there lurked.

Guinness was drunk, by most nursing mums
Made babies keen, to have their yum yums.
And should the babies, have the windies
In water you would dip red cinders.

For chilblains, I remember, once being told
Place, before you, two buckets one hot, one cold
Interchange feet, from the cold to the hot
Increasing the blood flow, through traumatic shock.

If you got a sting, mum dealt with it quick
She'd dab with blue dolly, the one on a stick.
Tea leaves were used, for poultice on face,
To ease pain from neuralgia, if this be the case.

A raw onion was peeled and in kitchen hung
To get rid of germs that struck at the lungs.
But if you were to faint, or slightly pass out,
Smelling salts were then held at your ungrateful snout

As medical care became more readily available to working-class people, the informal carers appear to have been replaced by the doctor and professional nurse. But they could still offer their services if medical science failed. One of these informal 'nurses' saved the life of one of Joan Miller's relatives. This is recorded in the continuation of the poem 'Remedies.'

But my mother-in-law told a true tale
How her little son Don once turned very pale.
The doctor was called, but his message was grim
He said he was sorry, but could do nothing for him.

For he had pneumonia, also rheumatic fever, too
Doctor said "I'm afraid very soon he will leave you"
Then a very old lady knocked on her door
Said "Can I try now, since he can't do more"

Then brown paper she wrapped all over his body,
Soaked slightly in paraffin, to make it grow soggy.
Don got through the crisis, during the night.
Come morning, the doctor was amazed at the sight.

He said "Thankfully Don is in danger no more"
And Mum blessed the old lady who'd knocked on her door.

(Joan Miller, work in progress.)

Gradually, informal community healers were replaced by professionals, such as district nurses, doctors and midwives (Oakley, 1979; Roberts, 1989; Adams, 1993). As the changes progressed, distinctions between professional care and informal care were made. Some writers have challenged this distinction, arguing that it masks the ways in which the two forms of care overlap (Waerness, 1990). Definitions about who are the experts can also be a problem. One of the informal carers interviewed argued that the experts are the people who are responsible for twenty-four hour care of the sick or infirm, regardless of their professional qualifications.

The impact this could have on families, in the future, is important due to the shift in recent years to care in the community. As we have argued in this chapter, like many other authors, there is nothing new about community care. The majority of sick and infirm have been cared for by their families for many years (Ratna and Davis, 1984).

Generally, the professionalism of care is progressive and positive, but it can have negative aspects, ie. by contributing to the gradual erosion of the existing informal networks of care. This means that future generations will probably not develop basic nursing skills (Waerness, 1990; Adams, 1993). Providers of informal care lose their potential to earn an independent income. For those who do manage to find work, this often has to be flexible and such employees lack the protection of other benefits, such as sickness pay and long-term pension plans. Thus, it is difficult for informal carers to ensure their own financial security in old age. Ironically, this is happening at a time when people are being encouraged to take out private pensions. Finally, people can be disadvantaged socially and medically by providing informal care, because this often confines them to the home. In a survey conducted by the National Association of Carers in the 1970s, it was found that many carers were unable to find time to go for hospital treatment on their own behalf.

Considering these individual factors, it seems a pity that the old informal carers have disappeared. In other ways, community care policies have advantaged those who provide informal care. For example, there is an increased emphasis on partnerships of care, in which professionals and receivers of services work together. The system may not be perfect, but it is a vast improvements on how things were during the early years of the National Health Service when there was little continuity of care between the hospital and the community.

The following account given by one of the older women illustrates an example of one calamity which developed due to this lack of continuation of care. The women describes the scene when her husband, following recovery from a stroke, was delivered by the ambulance men to his home.[6] The women explained that the ambulance men helped her husband to a chair in the couple's house. Following this they left. The couple spent a pleasant evening together and there appeared to be no problems, until the wife tried to put her husband into the bed which had been brought down stairs:

'Well I tried to lift him but he was a lot heavier than I expected, well...we struggled to get him across the room. Oh! It was killing my back, then he fell on top of me. Well it was terrible, he was on top of me and we couldn't move. Do you know, we were stuck there for most of the night...oh and we did cry because he couldn't move without help, and of course, I couldn't help him because I were trapped underneath him. Anyway, as luck would have it, Mrs Brown (a local woman who worked as an auxiliary nurse) had called to see her dad next door. He had said to her 'why Edith, Mrs Clarke's husband came home today.' He said, 'so get up yon will you to see if they need owt.' So she called, last thing as she were on her way home. Well, latch were off, because I'd not even managed to lock the door you know. So when she knocked and shouted, 'is everything all right?' I shouted 'Oh Mrs Brown, come in love, we're in a terrible state.' Well, without further ado, she come in, she got the fellah from next door to help, and they got him off me (the husband) then she tucked him up in bed, and settled us down. But

6   The woman cited was 86 years of age when interviewed in 1990. She explained that the events discussed took place in the mid 1960s.

before she left, she said, 'right Mrs Clarke, I think you've got a lot to learn and I'll come tomorrow to teach you.' So she came the next day, and she showed me how to get him out of bed, and from the bed to the commode, from the commode to the bed, from the bed to the chair. She taught us both, because she said there was no need at all for me to be taking all his weight like that, he could stand on his good leg you know. So she taught us both, and my poor husband were dizzy by the end of the day, he'd been lifted and moved so much he were dizzy...but by the time she left we knew what we were doing...now wouldn't it have helped if the hospital would have shown me all that?'

Research suggests that informal carers were active in many working-class communities well into the mid 1950s. It is true that people can pay for a nurse to come into the home to provide additional support, but this is not a service that everyone can afford. The informal carers belonged to a complex, close knit community, so that the cost of care could be negotiated. Payment could sometimes be made 'in kind', ie. in the form of food or goods. Informal carers could, it seems make a reasonable living for themselves. As autonomous practitioners, they could work and receive payment according to conditions of a service, which they had developed for themselves.

The disappearance of informal community carers may also be due to fragmentation of communities. The following discussion is based on interviews conducted by one of the authors on informal caring, past and present. The sample interviewed included twenty informal carers, two men and eighteen women, from the Bolton area. Interviews were conducted between the years of 1989–92. The transcript material used for this chapter concerns those who nursed a relative suffering from a terminal illness.

The older women interviewed explained that, up to the 1950s, some families in Bolton, particularly large families with several adult daughters, were able to provide care without the need for additional support. In many large families, care was shared between several family members and willing neighbours. But sweeping generalisations should be avoided. Some of the older women pointed out that, before the introduction of the National Health service, some carers could find the bulk of the responsibility resting on them[7]. Some of the carers interviewed said that they would have appreciated some practical or financial support during their experience as carers. However, most of the women interviewed cared because they wanted to, particularly if the sick person suffered from a terminal illness. The storyteller cited below[8] explains why she chose to care for her spouse when he was dying from lung cancer:

> 'We made it up when we were young, that if anything happened, we'd look after each other and not let either of us have to go into a home, it was a promise we made to each other years ago, when we were young.'

A younger woman speaking of caring for her late mother, explained that she was happy to do this rather than allow her mother to die in the care of strangers in the isolation of a hospital. The women explained the knowledge that she had done the very best she could for her mother, during the last few months of life was a source of great comfort to her after her mother had died:[9]

> 'And its not so bad you see, because at the end of the day you had them... and because of that they kept their dignity it's to do with how much respect you had for that person.'

The storyteller then recalled what happened when she left her mother in a home for respite care.

> 'I went to visit her, and I just felt like crying. I mean, they had her in this tight dress. I mean, I know they are busy and I'm not condemning them. You see, a nurse in a hospital doesn't know that person. I'm just the same. I mean when I nurse an old person, I don't think 'well just think, they were young once and they may have done this or that.' You just take them, as you see them as they are

---

7   It is depressing to note that little appears to have changed following the introduction of the National Health Service.

8   This woman was aged 50 years at the time of her interview in 1989.

9   This woman was aged 50 years at the time of her interview in 1989.

when you first meet them. But my mum, she was always a smart woman. Oh she was a very smart and handsome woman and very intelligent. She had her own business at a time when it was unusual for a woman to work. And you know, they (some of the staff in the respite home) were talking to her like she was a child. I know it's a very cruel thing to say, but it really made me angry. Because when she was young, when she was in her prime, she was smarter than most of those who were looking after her. I thought, 'your talking down to her like that, and I wouldn't mind but ten years ago she could have wrapped rings around every one of you lot, intellectually.'

During the time the woman cited above was nursing her mother, she was also running a home with teenage children to take care of and working part-time as an auxiliary nurse. Yet despite the multiple caring roles she was having to undertake, the storyteller still maintained that caring for her mother at home was the right thing to do. Coping with a long-term illness can make the surviving spouse (or carer) tired and resentful. But it can also help the carer come to terms with a bereavement (Bowling and Cartwright, 1995).

Several writers have commented in very negative ways on the transfer of the management of death from the home to the hospital (eg. Illich, 1977; Hockey, 1985). Some have argued that when older people move into a residential home, they become socially dead because their families and communities forget about them. Indeed it was concern for many of these issues which led to the growth of the hospice movement (Young, 1981). However, it is clear that many professional nurses do care deeply for their patients. A study by Field (1995) found that many nurses became emotionally involved with dying patients to the point where they cried at the death of the person they had been caring for. It is hard to believe that people who have such compassion for those they care for could be responsible for deliberately dehumanising them.

This illustrates some of the problems with feminists' theories that focus on the economics of informal caring. It is equally problematic to put woman's motivation to care down to socialisation or 'false consciousness.'[10] More recent feminist writers have acknowledged that people frequently care for others because they love the person they are caring for. There has also been an acknowledgement of the fact that caring relationships are too complex to be explained by economic considerations alone. For example, Finch and Groves (1983) have asked, 'would you put your sister in a home?'

When care was shared between several family members, apparently there could be an element of competition about who should be considered the main carer. One older woman recalled how a relative from another town, visiting the sick family member, gave some money to the caring female relative present during the visit. The storyteller met the visitor in the street as she walked away from the house. Below is her account of the meeting:

> *'She said she'd given our Edith some money cos she could see that she'd been working hard looking after dad. I said, 'You silly bitch!' What do you mean!' She's been doing nothing of the sort. Why it's me and our Lizzy who have been doing it all. Why she's only watching over him while I go t' shops. Well ..the barefaced so and so. Did she let you think that? She hardly does owt... it's me and our Lizzy. You silly bitch! You should have waited to see what was happening. Giving her all't credit like that... oh I were mad! She'd never been near for ages (the visiting relative) and then she comes and she's going away, giving all and sundry the wrong idea completely.'*

Unlike the younger women interviewed, the older carers did not complain of feeling socially isolated during their experience as carers. In Bolton, the demise of the cotton industry has led to a loss of the community spirit that was part of it. Therefore, it is quite inappropriate, at least on the basis of this study, to wish for a return to community care practices of the 'good old days.' Such a wish would reflect a nostalgic, but not necessarily accurate understanding of the past. Another point to make is that, even women who were accustomed to nursing people with physical ailments, reported

---

10   'False Consciousness' refers to the notion that women care not because they want to but rather because they have been socialised to believe that they ought to. This has many problems, ie. it does not explain why men may also choose to be carers.

distress if they had to care for a relative with mental health problems. This may be due to a phenomenon referred to by the Alzheimer's Disease Society as 'Living Bereavement.' Living bereavement refers to a situation in which people are caring for a relative whose personality has changed completely due to their condition. However, the women interviewed generally spoke of their experience in positive ways.

In conclusion, we have discussed the role of the informal community carer from the last century to more recent times and the methodological problems that made the reconstruction of their history difficult. There is limited archive material on the activities of informal carers during the last century. Sources of information that do exist are at risk of misinterpretation if people fail to take into account the social context. To develop the discussion, the writers have also drawn on interview material gathered by one of the authors.

Chapter 6
The layer-out

'It is an absolute requirement of Jewish law that the body (following a death) must be cleansed and made pure. Washing is usually performed by the Chevrah Kadish (burial society) through a religious ritual known as Taharah (purification). If there is no Chevrah Kadish, a rabbi should be consulted as non Jews are not allowed to perform the Taharah. Members of the family do not participate in the Taharah as it is considered too painful for them to bear.'

(Levine, 1997: 105)

'As soon as death has occurred the body is laid out on a hard surface, on the floor of the room or on a board placed on the bed. The feet are put together, the arms straightened along the sides, the eyes closed and the chin wrapped up with a piece of cloth. It is now that the body is washed. Sometimes the ablution is performed by close family members of the deceased but more often the washers, who usually act in pairs, are from a specialised trade. As a rule only men wash a man's body as only a women will wash a woman's body. They are paid for their services, although in some Arabic countries this is considered a modern abuse, as the services of washing a corpse counts as a pious deed.'

(Jonker, 1997: 153 — writing of the Islamic faith)

'Yes, I remember the layer-out. There were none left when I was a girl but I remember my mother telling me about them. The layer-out was a woman who used to come around laying out the dead. But when I was young, the family laid the person out. Every house had a laying out set when my mother was young. But when I was a girl they'd stopped worrying so much about everything being white and they would just put a clean shirt or night dress

71

on. The family would wash the body and tidy the bed like, then the neighbours would come to pay their last respects. People could pay their last respects right away or wait until the day of the funeral. My dad died in the night and my mother washed him and laid him out herself. She didn't trouble anyone till morning, she just sat with him all night. People didn't have the fear of the dead that they have today you see love? When the undertakers came for dad's body the day after, they said of my mother 'she's a brave little thing'. Apparently they were not used to that. People don't tend to lay their dead out now. They ring the doctor or undertaker and leave it to the professionals.'[1]

'I found my grandmother dead in the living room when I called to visit her. Did I lay her out, no way! I was frightened to death. I closed the door and called the undertaker. I leave things like that to the nurses and undertakers. Besides it was the first dead person I'd ever seen and I really was petrified.'[2]

Bereavement is a very painful process and the first few hours following a death can be the most difficult to bear. Our response to a death and, in particular, the corpse is shaped by social and cultural expectations and beliefs as well as our previous experiences of confrontations with death. We have already discussed some of the spiritual and subconscious aspects of laying-out. In this chapter, it is discussed in relation to caring and to continuing care in the community. In *Chapter 5*, we considered the informal community carer of the 1800s and the gradual development of professional care in the community. We continue our discussion of the care of the dying in the community, this time focusing on management of death and support for the bereaved family.

Several different professional groups now share the responsibility for care. Nurses, doctors and paramedics care for the dying and the mortician or funeral director cares for the corpse. The emotional support needed by a bereaved family or individual is a neglected aspect of care in present day

---

1   Bolton woman aged 60 years at the time of her interview in 1990.
2   Bolton woman aged 22 years at the time of her interview in 1995.

society. In the 1800s, there was no such fragmentation of care, at least in working-class communities.[3] Once a death had occurred in the family, the role of the informal carer would shift to that of the layer-out. The informal carer/layer-out could be a member of the deceased's own family or someone employed from outside. Provision of caring services by these informal carers meant that the sick person enjoyed as much dignity as possible during his/her illness, and was cared for in his/her own home. The services of the layer-out helped to maintain the family's dignity. In some cases, the services offered by the layer-out could help the family avoid the disgrace of a pauper's funeral (Roberts, 1989; Adams, 1993).

Chapter 5 discussed the methodological problems encountered when trying to construct a history of the informal carer. Because information on the layer-out is limited, writing this chapter has posed even greater difficulties. Some of the older people interviewed aged over 70 years did remember the layer-out but none interviewed had ever employed such a service. This is because the older people interviewed for this study, laid out their own dead. Information on the layer-out was also limited in the archive material available in Bolton Central Library.[4] However, the layer-out, like the informal carer, was referred to in some newspaper reports, such as the report recorded below.[5]

> '*A rare instance of generosity — At a meeting of the Bradford House of Industry, a few days ago, a woman applied for half-a-crown for laying-out a corpse of the parish to which the churchman said "Good woman, I think the money is too much for laying-out the corpse of this poor person, now what would you charge for laying*

3   The writer acknowledges that there were many vagrants and people without family support during the last century in Bolton. Our discussion therefore is a generalised account of what happened in many close knit communities. We also note that care of the dead could be offered by the community even in the case of vagrants (see the discussion in *Chapter 8*.

4   The author was told by a librarian at Bolton Central Library that the latter's grandmother remembered her neighbourhood layer-out.

5   *Bolton Chronicle*, 8th September, 1827.

out Dr X" (A Physician). "Half a guinea" said the woman. "And what would you charge for myself?" "Why" she rejoined. "I would do it for nothing and welcome!" This reply excited considerable merriment.'

This account suggests that the layer-out did not demand a fixed sum of money. Like the informal carers, the layer-out would negotiate the cost of care and the agreed fee would depend on the ability of families or the parish to pay, or on goodwill. Text-based information on the layer-out, such as that provided above, is rare and research on her activities has drawn on oral history sources. The work of the layer-out, if brought from outside the family, was quite detailed. Her practice included laying-out the corpse, consoling the bereaved family and sometimes helping them to save face. For example, if a family did not have a clean night-shirt, she would borrow one. Sometimes, the layer-out would help to arrange the funeral and she might even assist with the funeral tea (Roberts, 1989).

Some of the respondents interviewed gave very detailed accounts of the laying-out process, of the utensils and clothing used, of the appearance of the corpse and of the behaviour of the bereaved. Unlike the respondents interviewed by Adams (1993) and Roberts, the Bolton respondents were less likely to discuss the more intimate aspects of lying-out. Such practices included the binding of the body, the plugging of body orifices and the placing of pennies on the tummies of dead infants and on the eyes of the dead. Adams has drawn parallels between these practices and the care of infants, for example, the wrapping of babies and the placing of pennies on the tummy. She has also noted that much of the practice of the layer-out had sexual and spiritual overtones. One of the participants in this study (a woman aged 86 years when interviewed in 1989) remembered that the layer-out would sometimes place bags of salt on the bellies of women who had died in childbirth.

The Bolton interviewees were more likely to comment on the appearance of the corpse, emphasising in particular, its perceived humanity. The storyteller quoted below, for example, tells of a visitor's response to viewing the body of her dead spouse:

'*So he looked at him (the corpse) and he said "oh, sounds like he's snoring. He looks so peaceful, he looks really contented." Then, well you know, I had all the children up, and we had him in the parlour and they all came to sit awhile.*'

There are two possible reasons for apparent differences among the three studies. The first is the nature of the samples. The informants in Adam's study had no experience of having laid someone out themselves. Adam's sample had known or were related to a layer-out. When the Bolton interviewees spoke of laying-out, they were referring to someone they had known and had usually nursed prior to the death. The informants in Adam's study were speaking hypothetically of the corpse, whereas the Bolton sample spoke of their lived experience of dealing with a person. This may have been why so few of the Bolton sample (unlike those interviewed by Adams) spoke of the unpleasantness of having a dead person in the house, although there were exceptions.

'*I think most people were relieved when the undertaker took over. I mean, it wasn't very nice was it, having a dead body in the house? It's morbid and I suppose it could be very frightening as well, especially if you were living alone.*'

Kelly reported that for many families, particularly in the overcrowd households of the 1890s, having a corpse in the house could be not only unpleasant, but unhygienic. She writes that the poor would sometimes keep the corpse in the house for days while the bereaved family tried to get money together for a funeral. The corpse could be pulled about by children, objects could be rested on it, and it could even be used as a hiding placed for beer and gin bottles.

So it would seem that, despite any romantic nostalgia surrounding the concept of bodies being laid out at home in the past, there were probably many people who were only too happy to leave arrangements to the funeral director. However, the layer-out continued to prepare the body after death, even if the funeral director did oversee the final arrangements.

'Well way back, they were left at home until the funeral. The funeral director would send a woman, a 'layer-out' and she would wash the body and prepare it. Then they would bring along the coffin and they would put the body in the coffin. And there it would stay until the day of the funeral, that was usually about two or three days after the death.'

Other interviewees, such as the woman quoted below, felt that the involvement of the undertaker could be quite damaging because the body could be removed too quickly after the death had occurred.

'I think that the attitude today is all wrong. I mean the body is whisked off before you know it. People are naturally afraid if they haven't seen a dead person before so that it's understandable that they should feel in the first few hours that they should want to get rid of it. But I think that if they were given more time to come around they would probably get a lot of comfort. Not just from laying the body out, but from touching the body and having that last bit of contact before they say goodbye for ever. I mean there is no respect for the dead now. Everything is so rushed and the bereaved just do not have time to realise what has happened before the body's removed. I think that it's very sad now that people have such little contact with dead. I don't think that contact with the dead makes you morbid or afraid of death. But I do think that contact with the dead can give you a greater respect for life. It reminds you to live life to the full. Death is not real to people any more. They see it on the telly, but that does not make it real.' [6]

Overall, the people interviewed had quite varied ideas about who was qualified to attend to the dead in the first few hours after death. The stories of laying-out collected from the Bolton respondents, usually formed the conclusion of accounts of caring for a sick family member. In this context, the laying-out process was symbolic of what Graham (1983) refers to as a 'labour of love.' The woman, quoted below, gives an account of

6   55-year-old woman interviewed in 1995.

her family's role in caring for the father during a terminal illness and, after his death, laying him out.[7]

> *'Well she'd done all the washing (another sister). So she brought his clean shirt and got it ready, and we laid him out. And our Ken and Jenny (another sister and her spouse) were in and Jenny said, 'when did he die' and we said 'about an hour ago.'*

The simplicity of the described scene is quite moving. There was an expectation that witnesses of the death bed scene should observe 'proper' behaviour and conduct. There was strong disapproval in some families for overt and dramatic displays of grief. This is shown in the following account given by one of the interviewees about an outburst of emotion displayed by a family member at a death bed scene:

> *'And Jenny said "get a mirror, get a mirror" and I said, "what do we need with a mirror?" Anyrowds, I give her one. "See! See!" she said, "he's alive, he's still breathing" (the deceased). Our Tom said "don't be daft...he's dead, you can see he's dead!' ...Get out o road" (this in response to the grieving woman trying to prevent her sisters from lying out the dead man). She said "Ho...No! No! No!" And I thought "what a paraphernalia"...I mean, he was dead, you could see he was dead OOH! And she carried on, on and on that he wasn't dead...and our Alice said "oh ek." I mean, really, you never saw a carry on like it in all your life.'*

The storyteller's judgmental attitude towards her sister may seem harsh, but reflects the matter-of-fact attitude towards death, common to many of the older women interviewed by the author of this book. Moreover, such displays may threaten the notion of the serene and peaceful 'good death' which Aries has recorded as being important. The family's disapproval of such an open display of grief is understandable from this perspective. Disapproval of overt displays of grief did not apply only to those acted out at the death bed. Another storyteller, cited below, gives an equally condemning account of an

7   This woman was aged 88 years at the time of her interview in 1990.

out-burst by one of her sisters, when informed of a sister-in-law's sudden death as she returned from church.[8]

> *'Well we were just coming back from church when this neighbour of ours came over. And she said "hast heard the awful news? Why your Mary's dropped dead." Well she (one of the sisters) threw her arms up like this (mimics) and she said "Oh dear" and she was shouting and carrying on...in't street mind. Why, they were all looking... But she didn't bother.. I suppose you would call it dramatic effect like.... Well, she ran up street to our Jack's. I thought, "poor lad, as if he's not enough to put up with without all this." You know, her carrying on like that, I mean, poor Mary not even cold in her grave, why it was a sin!'*

Those who are unfamiliar with family life in Bolton, may read with surprise that these recollections reflected considerable affection for the more emotional sister. However, the families who took part in the study had lived their lives in very close proximity and supported each other steadfastly. Life was a more communal existence than that found in the modern, nuclear family. Laungani (1995), in his discussion of Indian family life, reminds us that when families share a close communal arrangement, it is natural for people to get 'fed up' with each other from time to time. In such situations, arguments and emotional outbursts of anger are to be expected. Nowadays, many people die in hospital. Caring for a dying relative at home can still be a more positive experience than is possible in an institution. Given that the informal carers and the layer-out no longer offer their services, a sympathetic district nurse can help a carer through the dying process. This is illustrated by the following extract from one of the interviews:

> *'His sister, she had come down that day to give him a wash and a shave, you know. She was helping me out, anyrowds, she lathered up this side of his face (indicated left side of face) and he got hold of my hand and he said 'I*

8   The interviewee quoted was 84 years of age at the time of her
     interview in 1988.

*love you, I love you'. And he was stroking my hand like
this and then, oh it was lovely, he got hold of my hand
and he said 'I love you'. And then he pulled me over and
he gave me the most lovely kiss and within one hour of
him giving me that kiss he was dead.'*

It is very unlikely that the widow quoted above would have
enjoyed such intimacy with her husband during his last few
hours had his death taken place in a hospital. The woman
quoted above did have a district nurse present during the time
described and, from the way in which the interviewee
described her behaviour, she appeared to have dealt with the
matter extremely well. For example, the nurse distanced
herself during the scene cited above, making herself busy in
the kitchen. After the death the interviewee told how the
nurse came into the room and offered practical and emotional
support to the widow and her sister-in-law after the death.

This scene provides us with an example of how a
sympathetic professional can be a great source of comfort and
support to the bereaved. Another widow told a very different
story. Her spouse died in the 1970s, just before nursing
education included subjects, such as bereavement counselling
and support in the curriculum. This widow explained that the
district nurse in her case, came into the house. Since the
widow's spouse had died, she simply laid him out without
saying a word and then left. From the widow's account, she
was unable to grasp the fact that her spouse had died. She
explains that she:

*'tried to give him some medicine, but it sort of stuck in his
throat. I felt his hands and they were cold, and then I put
my hands under the covers to feel his belly, and that was
still warm.'*

Eventually, the widow went into the street. She asked a
passerby whether or not they had ever seen a dead person
before. The passerby answered in the affirmative so the widow
asked the stranger into the house to give an opinion. This
story does need to be interpreted with some caution. Clearly,
the widow was in a state of shock following her husband's
death and her recollections of the event may not be completely
accurate. Numbness and denial are common reactions in the

bereaved during the hours following a death (Parkes, 1972; Bowlby, 1980). It does seem that, despite these considerations, the district nurse had little understanding of the grieving process. She appears to have lacked the ability to empathise with the bereaved person, or to have had sufficient insight into her own attitude to death, to manage the situation appropriately.

This example raises questions about the education of nurses and the need recognised by many writers to improve and diversify nursing training beyond the medical model. Nurse education in recent years is responding to this need, drawing not only from the social sciences, but also the arts and literature (Rose and Parker, 1994; Schroeder-Skeder, 1994; Moyle *et al*, 1995). More recent nursing models do not restrict themselves to the more cognitive (intellectual) approaches and are more holistic (Bertman and Krant, 1977; Benner and Tanner, 1987; Dhalberg, 1989). Many nursing models are informed by the philosophies of humanistic and existential psychology (Benner, 1989; Johns, 1993).

It is now considered important that the education of any caring professional should include some element of personal reflection and growth. This is why many nurses are encouraged to keep a reflective diary during their education (Johns, 1993).[9] Some writers have shown that if theory is taught in a simplistic way, there is a risk that nurses will apply it inappropriately (Kalish, 1985; Kastenbaum, 1972). Keeping a reflective diary can help because it encourages nurses think more judiciously about the application of theory to practise. The author has been conducting research with enrolled nurses completing a conversion course. The nurses interviewed had been encouraged to keep a reflective diary during the course and found this very helpful. Current practice considers that counselling skills are an important part of nurse education, and practitioners in all the caring professions are more sensitive to the needs of the bereaved.

9   A reflective diary is a personal diary kept by the nurse in which she is encouraged to record significant experiences in her work, reflect on these experiences and use them as a basis to learn from them.

Conclusion

In this chapter, we have considered the management of the corpse in the hours following a death, the role of the layer-out in the past and the current role of the professional. There was a varied response to the question of who should be responsible for the care of the corpse in the hours following the death. The answers depended upon the level of experience people had of bereavement. It was more common in the recent past for bodies to be laid out at home, by the family or layer-out. However, from this study, age does not appear to make a difference to people's feelings about who should deal with the corpse after death. Of the older people interviewed, some reported a sense of relief when the undertaker took over the management of the body. Others disapproved, feeling that the present fear of death is caused because people have little contact with the dead. In the following chapters, we continue our discussions on death in relation to the funeral.

Chapter 7
The pauper funeral

Chapter 9 describes the finery, celebration and display, which is characteristic of many northern funerals. Before exploring these death rituals, it is important to consider some of the variables that shaped their evolution. There are conflicting opinions about the emotional and social value of funerals and these are explored in greater depth in *Chapter 9*. However, in this chapter, it is appropriate to consider the opinion of writers, such as Cannadine who is quite dismissive of the concept of the Victorian celebration of death. He argues that the expensive and lavish funerals, characteristic of that era probably caused many families problems and anxiety.

Those who believe in the beneficial and therapeutic effects of a funeral may disagree with Cannadine, but work by other researchers, such as Richardson, suggests that he makes some very good points. All rituals are influenced by a combination of issues. In this and the following chapter, we discuss two issues that helped to shape working-class people's perceptions of the meaning and importance of funerals. These two issues are the threat of dissection after death, caused by the Anatomy Law of 1832 (Richardson, 1988) and fear of the pauper funeral.

Richardson has described what she refers to as the 'nest egg' phenomena. She identified the concern of some older people that they should save enough money to cover the cost of their funeral. These savings remained untouched despite financial hardship. Not all nest egg savers had bank accounts, preferring to keep the money in their house and sometimes on their own person. This exposed older people to the risk of attack from criminals who might try to steal such nest eggs. People were concerned that, in the event of their death, a friend or relative should be aware of the existence of the money and the purpose for which it had been saved — burial. This led them to confide in others who were not necessarily discrete or even trustworthy. In sharing such confidences, older people placed themselves at risk of being burgled or attacked, particularly if they lived alone.

Richardson found that the typical nest egg conserver was usually female, aged 70 years and older. She had usually experienced financial hardships, frequently during her childhood or teenage years. Richardson attributed the nest egg phenomena to the fear of the pauper funeral. In this respect, Richardson's work is of particular interest to the writers of this book. Many older Boltonians also had a 'nest egg' saved to cover the cost of their funeral. These older people shared the characteristics identified by her and for the same reasons. Indeed, some explicitly referred to recollections of paupers' funerals from their youth. One of the individuals interviewed recalled how, as a very young boy, he had seen a group of men carrying a coffin down the street. Even at this young age, he knew that this meant the family could not afford a hearse, and that this was shameful and humiliating.

Another individual[1] spoke of a family who had never recovered from the disgrace of having to provide a 'cheaper' funeral for their late father. Apparently, this was not even in the strictest sense, a pauper's funeral because the family had managed to purchase a plot for the grave and a cheap coffin. The family had needed to cut the cost of the funeral by burying the dead man in one of his old night-shirts rather than a shroud. In addition, the sons had to dig the grave and carry the body, in the coffin, to the nearby cemetery. The event reported probably took place in the early part of this century.

All the older Boltonians interviewed had a sum of money put by to cover the cost of burial, and some had been saving for years. Each storyteller commented on the difficulties that saving this money could cause:

> 'Well, I have ter bury meself when owt happens to me, you know. So you have to save to be buried don't you? You can't die and then let the town bury you, after you've lived 80 odd years. No! They expect you to bury yourself. but they don't know what's happened to you in your life, they don't know where your moneys gone or anything.'

1   This woman was aged 86 years at the time of her interview in 1990.

The woman quoted above appeared to be experiencing a great deal of ambivalence during her interview. She explained that she had been brought up to take responsibility for her life. But as she had grown older, she had realised that life could be very unpredictable. A person could be sensible and responsible, ie. save to cover the cost of his/her own burial, but despite this, might still need to be buried by the parish, because the money saved was needed to pay for necessities prior to death.

This supports the point made by Richardson in the conclusion of her 1988 paper, in which she states that many older people have to deal with two sets of opposing principles. Many older people in England have grown up with the belief that they should provide the money to pay for their own funeral. They place a high value on a 'good funeral', ie. the very best they can afford. People of the present generations are more likely to spend money on living rather than death.

Another woman[2] recalled her distress because she and her late spouse had saved for most of their adult lives to ensure that they would have a decent burial. Unfortunately, they spent the money on an operation which the husband was unable to obtain on the National Health Service:

'I reckon it was an untold sin that we were having to pay all that money for his operation, and still we'd worked all our lives. I'd worked in't mill, my daughter was only little when I went back to work, and I worked till I were 64. And when he finished up (retired) he were in agony with his leg, and I say its a sin for people to save up all their lives to be buried and then have to pay it all out to pay for things like that (the husband's operation). I had to pay two thousand pounds, as I would save up to have us buried, and then it never worked, he died just after, and then I had ter borrow to bury him. I were shown up like that, and we'd worked and saved all our lives.

The researcher asked some of the older Boltonians what they thought about the rising cost of funerals. For some this was causing considerable anxiety. But for others, the cost of the

2   This woman was aged 90 years when interviewed in 1989.

funeral to give some they loved a decent burial did not appear to concern them very much.[3] As one woman put it:

> *'I mean, you are too upset aren't you. People don't ask about the cost when it's someone they love. And I mean anyway, that's life isn't it, it's dear when you come into the world and it's dear when you go out.'*

The Boltonians interviewed were over the age of seventy years and could remember the introduction of the National Health Service and the Welfare State. Although they spoke of these changes in very positive ways, the transcript material from their interviews reflected the strong ethos that people should take financial responsibility for their own life and death. This emphasis on personal responsibility was a characteristic that many people of this age group shared. It appears to stem from the belief that asking the Welfare State for assistance was similar to asking for charity. In her autobiography, Andrews writes of the perceptions she and a friend had of the Welfare State when it was first introduced:

> *'The Welfare State was too young for either of us to have outgrown the conviction, deeply ingrained in all British social classes, that all public assistance was charity and existed only to help only the physically disabled and poor. So ingrained and widespread was the belief that even when an individual was poverty stricken, it remained the fundamental responsibility of that individual to right the situation as best he or she could by his or her efforts.'*

(Andrews, 1977)

However, the word 'responsibility' covers a wide range of issues. Clearly the concept of what one ought to take responsibility for differed between the younger Bolton people interviewed and the older group. The older individuals interviewed were less concerned about taking responsibility for preventing ill health in later life. This may have been due to the age of the individuals. Even taking age into account, there seemed to be a view expressed by some that ill health

3   Aged 86 years at the time of her interview in 1993.

was an inevitable part of growing old. Indeed, when casually asked during her interview about steps taken to care for her own health, one eighty-five years old confused this with vanity:

> *'Well I don't know, I mean you have to grow old gracefully. I mean, I don't believe in all this colouring your hair and stuff. I mean, there's all this worry about losing your teeth and stuff now, I mean when I was young most women lost all their teeth when they had their babies. I mean, I'm not saying that we should go back to that now, but I mean now they will hang on to their teeth even when they're causing them loads of pain...well, I think it's better to just have them out. I mean, there's all this shame at having to wear dentures, why when I was young you were lucky if you could afford dentures. Most if they lost their teeth had to walk around toothless altogether.'*

Others adopted the attitude that looking after one's health long-term was reasonable in moderation. In recent years the emphasis has changed to prevention rather than cure, and this has led to the development of health promotion and education, in the health professions. Such apparently deterministic attitudes towards ageing and ill health in the older women, is hardly surprising and we raise these points for two reasons.

Reference is frequently made to the principle of taking responsibility for one's life. This can be discussed in a very general way and people rarely consider its complexity. People may take responsibility for some aspects of their lives but not others. This is relevant to the discussion because many older individuals saved a great deal of money for a decent funeral. People in the nineties may consider that this money would be better spent on a good, nutritious diet, or dental bills in order to retain a full set of teeth. This attitude was taken by the middle- and upper-classes during the nineteenth century towards the poor. Despite the apparently ill-advised tendency to save for funerals, even when times were hard, older people had good reason to fear a pauper burial.

Given the importance attached to funerals during the Victorian era by all social classes, it seems surprising that so many of the upper-classes had little tolerance for the fear of a pauper funeral that was experienced by working-class people. Samuel Smiles, for example, was quite dismissive of the desire of the poor, to bury their dead with dignity, considering this to be little more than show. Smiles was, generally, unsympathetic towards the poor. He believed it was their moral failings that caused their position in society, since 'any class of man that lives from hand-to-mouth will ever be an inferior class.' It could be argued that the source of Smiles condemnation, was lack of understanding of the difficulties faced by the poor, whom he considered merely 'thriftless persons.' He wrote:

'They waste their money as they do their time, draw bills upon the future, anticipate their earnings, and are thus under the necessity of dragging after them a load of debts and obligations which seriously effect their actions as free and independent men.'

Most of the interviews conducted for this book were with older women. It is difficult to estimate the accuracy of Smiles' description of working-class men. However, the Bolton women in this sample, who had all spent their working lives in the textile industry, could hardly be accused of 'wasting their money as they do their time.'

What is depressing is the striking similarity of the thinking reflected in the extract above, with that of many commentators on the poorly paid and unemployed at the present time. It seems that we really have come full circle, having turned back almost completely to the 'Victorian Values' of writers such as Smiles. Interestingly, many of these judgmental commentaries insist that the unemployed of today are different from those of the past because the latter wanted to work.

This lack of understanding and empathy for the plight of the poor, could be demonstrated even by those who advocated a more sympathetic approach, such as Margaret Loane writing in the 1800s (cited by Johnson, undated paper, see *Footnote 4*):

'Broadly speaking, the people who become and remain rich are those who accept all the responsibilities that life brings them.'

There is an inclination to wonder how, within such a conceptual framework, Loane would have explained some of the issues discussed in *Chapter 5* concerning the poverty of women caused by their readiness to take on caring responsibilities. Wilson and Levey, writing in 1938 did show a much deeper level of understanding, particularly in relation to the pauper funeral:

> '*Though a pauper funeral may be 'decent', it is still felt to be a slur on the dead and their relatives. The feeling of shame aroused by the common grave are enhanced by the idea that such internment represents the loneliness of a corpse for whom nobody cares about accept the Poor Law Authority, who are simply fulfilling a statutory or sanitary obligation. These feelings are, to our knowledge, as strong as ever today. The poorer the individual, the lower in the social scale, the deeper the sense of guilt and shame if he cannot promise a decent burial for his relatives.*'

During the nineteenth century, people from all social classes were indoctrinated about the 'evil' and 'shame' of the pauper's funeral from a very early age. A study of popular nineteenth century children's magazines conducted by Dixon (1989) shows that even very young children during the Victorian and Edwardian period were socialised to accept the importance of a decent funeral. Typical stories in such journals would tell of (and present as the norm) families who had sold every stick of furniture in order to pay for the burial of their dead. Significantly, such stories were not presented as tragedies, but rather, as a 'matter-of-fact' account of what was sometimes necessary. The tragedies which were reported often related to those unfortunate deceased who, having failed to save for their funeral in life, had, in death, no surviving relatives who cared enough to pay. Dixon cites in her 1989 paper, the following extract from the children's journal Peter Parley's Annual published in 1868:

> '*In a few days the corpse of the poor woman was put into a shell and taken away to the common burial ground at the* **expense** *(my emphasis) of the parish. It was carried in a*

*chimney sweep's cart. There was mourning only of the
sooty kind. There were no pall bearers.'*

In the extract above, we are given some insight into the
loneliness of the corpse commented on by Wilson and Levey.
However, this was a perceived loneliness. A corpse is not a
person and thus, is incapable of feeling anything at all, least of
all lonely. The real disgrace summarised above, is not the
loneliness of the corpse but rather the expense its disposal had
caused the parish. In the nineteenth century, people were
socialised from a very early age, not to cause expense to the
parish. So it is little wonder that the fear of a pauper's funeral
became ingrained by the time people reached adulthood.

Moreover, in cases where families had to resort to a
pauper funeral for their dead, the actual methods of disposal
could cause great distress to the bereaved. Richardson writes
of the pauper funeral that it provided the bare minimum. The
body, wrapped in paper or calico, was placed in a coffin made
from the cheapest wood, lined with sawdust. Sites for the
paupers' mass graves were usually situated next to the
poorhouse, or in the worst part of the cemetery. The graves
were usually about 20 coffins deep and 10 coffins wide.
Quicklime was sprinkled over the coffins to speed up the
process of decay so that the graves could be reused as quickly
as possible. The bereaved had no say as to when the funeral
was to take place or where their deceased were to be buried.
There was no religious service held for the dead.

The desire to avoid a pauper funeral led many
working-class people to take out death insurance during the
nineteenth century.[4] According to Johnson the amount saved
by the average family rarely amounted to more than 2d a
week, since those who took out such insurance were mainly
factory workers and hardly ever from the higher social classes.
Child insurance was particularly popular because of high
infant mortality. Yet despite this, the insurance companies
made quite a profit on child death insurance (Johnson,
undated paper).

4   Johnson E (undated) 'Saving and spending: The Working Class
     Economy in Britain: 1870–1939' Source, Bolton Central Library,
     Local History Section, Bolton, Lancs.

The articles for the Union Insurance Company, in Bolton, shows that some societies had very strict guidelines to ensure that no member would obtain money by fraudulent means. Each head of a family had to subscribe to paying the company ninepence a month, until the stock amounted to twenty pounds. Members over forty years of age with more than four children in the family, had to pay a further 2d a week to cover each child above that number. Members under the age of thirty-five years of age could cover up to five children at no extra cost, but any additional children required the family pay the additional 2d.

All live children born to society members had to be recorded within the insurance provision within 48 hours following the birth. Members could be excluded from the society for failing to provide evidence of any ill health in family members covered by the insurance, as is the case with many insurance companies today. Members could also be excluded for entering under the cover, non-existent children — presumably, such children had a habit of 'dying.'

Providing that the members followed the rules and paid their dues in full, in the event of a child death in the family, they would receive 5 shillings for a child under five, 30 shillings for children who died between the ages of 5 and 10 years and 50 shillings if the child had been between the ages of 10 and 15 years of age. In the event of the death of children over the age of 15 and adults, the family would receive £3.

The high mortality rates of the time, and the cost of a funeral, must have presented a considerable burden for families. So these insurance companies probably did provide a very useful service to the poor. However, the services which they provided could, apparently, be abused.

Kelly reports that during the latter part of the nineteenth century, infanticide was quite common and, in some families predictable. She writes that it was not uncommon when a child was born, for neighbours to note that the infant, having been registered for death insurance, would probably not live long. Other writers have commented on the concern that infanticide was motivated by a desire to claim death insurance (eg. Fielding, 1994). So, it was clearly a social concern at the time. However, Roberts concluded that for many families, actually finding the money from a meagre wage to pay for death insurance, could be a source of strain. So how profitable such crimes would be is difficult to speculate. Certainly, many women were convicted and executed for this crime (Fielding, 1995). Some of those convicted of this crime may have been innocent. Arsenic was used in the nineteenth century as a disinfectant to cleanse the filthy, disease-ridden hovels in which many working-class families lived. Given the lack of knowledge about the correct and safe use of this substance, it is quite possible that some mothers accidentally poisoned their children and other members of the family.

Richardson points out that there is still a stigma attached to the pauper funeral. Paupers are usually cremated rather than buried. Cheaper funerals are dealt with haphazardly and hastily, and are often referred to by some funeral directors as the 'nine-o-clock trot.' As society becomes more fragmented, people feel less compulsion to pay for the burial of a deceased relative who they hardly knew when alive (see *Chapter 9*). This reluctance to pay for expensive funerals could occur in cases where the deceased has left sufficient money to cover the cost of burial. Many such 'bereaved' families prefer to opt for the cheapest funeral possible and use the money left by the deceased for other purposes. We need to be cautious about judging such behaviour. Values have changed and for some families it makes more sense to use inherited money for the living rather than the dead.

This chapter concludes with the point made by Richardson, that the fear of a pauper funeral during the last century could be related to fear of the body snatchers. The body snatchers stole corpses and sold them to anatomists for dissection. They posed a threat to bereaved families from the Georgian period onwards. The corpses of the poor were particularly vulnerable to this practice because of the flimsy coffins and the custom of leaving pauper graves uncovered until full. Body snatchers are discussed in the next chapter.

Chapter 8
The resurrectionists

On February 6th, 1830, the following article appeared in the Bolton Chronicle:

> *Body Stolen — The body of a man known as 'Old Tom' and who went about begging and selling matches was stolen on Monday evening under the following circumstances. The deceased had lodged for some time past in King Street but, not being able to satisfy the claims of his landlady, he was turned out and, early on Thursday evening week, he was found lying in Deansgate, nearly frozen to death, and was conveyed to the house of a poor women, who resided in the yard behind the Lord Collingwood Public House, where he lingered until Sunday, when he expired. The house next to where the man die, happening to be.... the body was placed on a door and removed to it until a coffin could be produced. About nine-o-clock on Monday evening, three men, who had the appearance of travelling tinkers and who professed to be relations of the deceased, requested permission to see the body, which was granted and they shortly afterwards left the premises, but in less than quarter of an hour they returned and gave the alarm that the body was missing. This on examination proved to be the case, and notwithstanding every search has been made, it has not been heard of. The tinkers, after giving the alarm, walked off and cannot be found. Old Tom was well known about the town, from the circumstances of him having two wooden legs. He was we understand, a native of Staffordshire, and received a weekly allowance from some parish in that county; he had in the early part of his life been employed in the main fishery on the Greenland coast, and from the effects of the cold, was necessitated to have both his legs amputated below the knee. This affair has created a great sensation in the town, and the night watch at the old church yard has been doubled.*

The story above illustrates a number of points and that is why it has been presented in its entirety. The first and most obvious, is that it illustrates the terrible poverty in which many people of the time lived their lives. Indeed, on the same day that the case of Old Tom was reported, the same paper reported the case of a woman who collapsed in a public house. She had left her children in the local poor house and then went to the public house where she collapsed, to beg for some assistance. The woman later died. The cause of death was reported to have been that of 'want of the basic necessities of life.'

Yet there was a positive side to the hardships endured by the communities of Bolton during the last century. The people were capable of considerable kindness and compassion. Also worth considering, is the degree of tolerance to people who were different or eccentric. The events described occurred in the year 1830, just prior to the rise of the institutions for the insane and the removal of all those considered mad from the community. Old Tom, the report suggests, was a bit of a character and, had he lived at the present time, might have been considered a person with mental as well as physical health problems. Yet despite his infirmities, he managed to get by on his wits and from the account we can assume, he did so quite well. It is true that the unfortunate man did eventually die homeless and frozen by the cold. Writing this chapter over a hundred years later, it is depressing to consider that his plight is similar to that of many of the homeless today — the young, old, infirm and those evicted into the street in the name of so-called community 'care.'

The difference between Old Tom and many of our homeless today is that, despite his destitution, he was shown some affection during his last hours. Old Tom, frozen and near dead, may well have understood as his life ended, that he belonged to and was a part of that community of people who carried him to the old woman's house to die in some warmth and comfort. Old Tom was a pauper. If his body had not been seized by the Resurrectionists (or body snatchers), it would probably have ended in one of the large common paupers' graves. Old Tom did not even have the luxury of a community resting place. The fact that he was denied this last token of dignity in death, caused, as the article reports, public outrage and disgust.

In the preceding chapter, we discussed how many middle-class people had little understanding, sympathy or tolerance for working-class people's concern for a decent funeral for their dead. This lack of tolerance may seem quite reasonable given the poverty and hardship in which so many people lived their lives. In Bolton, a good funeral was a symbol of respect, not just to the deceased, but also to the bereaved family. The funeral in many of the working-class communities of the time provided an opportunity to celebrate the life of the deceased. The pomp and ceremony of the funeral gave working-class families a status and dignity in death, far removed from that accorded in life. A pauper funeral was bad enough. Having one's body stolen for the purpose of dissection was, for the poor, and the not so poor, an even greater horror. This fear of dissection could be related to Christian doctrines concerning resurrection. As discussed in *Chapter 7*, this fear reinforced many people's dislike of cremation.

Having discussed the resurrectionists, or body snatchers, explored the social context in which they operated and the Anatomy Law of 1832 that led to their disappearance, we conclude by discussing the work of Hannah, a resurrectionist who was active in the trade of body snatching in Bolton during the late 1820s and early 1830s. As the years of the Enlightenment progressed, it became increasingly recognised that, if medical knowledge was to advance at all, a knowledge and understanding of anatomy was necessary. This knowledge could only be acquired and passed to other doctors by the dissection of corpses. Religious concerns made many people reluctant to donate their bodies to medical science. This religious concern for the sanctity and power of the corpse has roots deep in western culture, and existed prior to the dominance of Christianity in the western world.

The word 'necromancer' is derived from the Greek word 'nekros' meaning a corpse. A necromancer was a sorcerer who could reveal future events or disclose secrets by communicating with the dead. Dissection involves communication of a kind with the dead in which the secrets of the body were revealed to medical men. Many stories of witchcraft include descriptions of practices that occurred on graves or around cemeteries (Summers, 1995). Some writers have argued that the witch hunts coincided with the growth of the medical profession in the fourteenth century. In the eighteenth century, medical men become involved in one of the practices for which the witches had been condemned — interfering with the dead.

Added to religious concerns, was the fear of dissection caused by the introduction of a law in 1752, which stipulated that all murderers were to be dissected following execution. This law had been passed because of George II's concerns that:

> *'The horrid crime of murder has of late been more frequently perpetuated, and particularly in and near the Metropolis, contrary to the known humanity and natural genius of the British Nation, and that it has therefore become necessary that some further terror and particular mark of infirmity be added to the punishment of death, now by law in such as shall be guilty of the said heinous offence.'*

The concerns expressed by the King at that time was to lead Parliament to conclude that the following deterrent be added to the punishment of hanging for murder:

> *'It is accordingly enacted, that persons found guilty of wilful murder, shall be executed the day next but one after sentence is passed, and that the body shall then be given for dissection; unless the judge should appoint it to be hung in chains, but in no case whatever is the body of a murderer to be buried without being first dissected or anatomised.'*

This added indignity was considered a suitable deterrent because:

> *'The prompt execution of the criminal, followed by hanging in chains or dissection, would seem calculated to striking a wholesome terror to persons so brutalised, as to be insensible to the dread and horror of murder which nature has implanted in the human heart as a protection for human life.'*

Dissection then, posed a threat to the resurrection of the person after death and also had terrible connections to the gallows. The societal rejection of the criminal, even in death, was symbolised by violation of the body. Despite the views expressed by the ruling-class, however, the general public felt as much revulsion and outrage at the violation of the corpse of a murderer, as they did for anyone else. This sense of outrage was well illustrated in the conclusion of newspaper reports of the execution of two convicted murders, Milton and Magrath, in 1829:[1]

> *'The bodies were suspended for an hour, and then removed under strong guard to the College of Surgeons for the purpose of dissection. When the bodies were cut down, the people hooted the police; and no one would assist the jailer in putting the bodies into the cart.'*

It is hardly surprising that there was a shortage of corpses for dissection. Religious influences led many people to develop a fear and general sense of revulsion towards it. In addition there was the attached stigma because, before the Anatomy Act of 1832, the only corpses that anatomists could legally obtain were those of criminals from the gallows. Yet despite the public disdain for dissection, there appears to have been a fascination for anatomy that was similar to the attitude to the Pornography of Death discussed by Gorer. Gorer argues that, during the twentieth century, people are so shielded from the experience of death and dying that, as a result, their perceptions of it have become unrealistic and distorted. We recoil from direct confrontations with death, but are entertained by media images that are explicit and exaggerated. This same 'peep show' mentality appears to have been characteristic of people's attitude to human biology during the 1800s. A newspaper article of 1843, for example, announced a forthcoming human anatomy exhibition in the following way:[2]

> *'FIRST VISIT OF SIGNIOR SARTIS CELEBRATED FLORENTINE VENUS; There is no mystery into which*

1   *Bolton Chronicle*, 14th November, 1829.
2   *Bolton Free Press*, 20th June, 1843.

mankind are more anxious to pry into than into that of their internal structure, and certainly there is none on earth which can so nearly concern them. Everyone must have felt in reading descriptions of the human frame and its various organs, how difficult it is to acquire a satisfactory knowledge from them, even from the plainest account.'

The first part of the article above seems quite objective and logical. One only has to read the tiny print of some of the newspapers of the time to realise that printed material was probably quite expensive so that illustrated human biology books were probably quite rare. However, it is not so much the argument that an understanding of human biology is desirable, but the way in which the 'exhibition' was publicised.[3] The report continues:

'The exquisite figure, which will remain on view for a short period only, clears up all the difficulties at once. The Florentine Venus — a full length figure which takes to pieces from head to foot, exhibiting with wonderful accuracy, the whole of the human figure. Its excellence in anatomical merit is acknowledged by the most eminent scientific and medical men in the country.'

The publication of the 'exhibition' presents something of a contradiction. Here we have scientific rationality with pornographic undertones. Indeed, the very naming of a medical doll as 'The Florentine Venus' suggests a naughtiness most people today might consider infantile at the very least. That the 'exhibition' might provide something like the porcelain equivalent of a man in a raincoat, is confirmed by the concluding sentence:

'Ladies' days — Tuesdays and Fridays.'

In this context, body snatching became a lucrative business for those people (referred to at the time as 'Resurrectionists') who had no qualms about stealing corpses in order to make a living. Corpses could bring anything from 8 to 16 guineas. The fee for

3   The 'exhibition' in this case amounted to little more than the
      presentation of a life-sized, pull-apart doll.

a child's corpse was paid according to length (Richardson, *op cit*). The resurrectionists often worked in teams, invading the cemeteries at night and using wooden spades to dig up corpses of the recently deceased (Kelly, 1988).

They had no respect for the rich or poor, being happy to take whatever corpses came their way. People took out all manner of after life insurance and paid huge sums of money to undertakers to ensure that their corpse would not end up in the clutches of the body snatchers or anatomists. Richardson writes that one factor, contributing to the profits which could be made on the funeral service, was the threat of the resurrectionists. Many funeral directors of the Georgian period, advertised as part of the service 'body snatch safe' devices for which the rich were willing to pay large sums of money. However, many were paying for a false sense of security. Some, less ethical, funeral directors increased their profits substantially by burying weighted coffins and despatching the corpse to the anatomist's table.

The corpses of the poor were more vulnerable to the threat of the resurrectionists because their coffins were so flimsy. A report[4] in 1832, of the snatching of the corpse of a late Betty Dodd, revealed that her coffin was so fragile, the resurrectionists did not even try to open it, but instead simply split the lid. Paupers' graves were even more vulnerable. Kelly writes that, in Bolton, pauper graves were often left open until full and resurrectionists did not have to dig to remove the bodies. Another pauper's grave discussed by Kelly consisted of a huge vault in one of the chapels with the capacity to hold between 20 and 30 bodies. A few boards covered the grave until it was filled and properly sealed.

Richardson writes that poorer people in many communities organised self-help groups. These were teams who worked in shifts to guard the body until it became so decomposed that it would useless to the anatomists. An example of this practice reported by Kelly, concerned a local mill owner, Thomas Rothwell. When he died, workmen from his mill worked in shifts to guard his grave in Holy Trinity for several weeks to ensure that his body would not be stolen. In

4   *Bolton Chronicle*, 7th January, 1832.

some areas, vigilante groups sought out the resurrectionists who, if discovered, could be badly beaten — sometimes to death. Richardson writes that, although some vigilantes were brought before the courts, implicit support for what they were doing was reflected in the light sentences meted out. High railings were erected to surround graveyards and heavy gates placed at the entrance to make access difficult. For those who could afford it, heavy stone slabs were placed over the grave. Straw was mixed into the soil to make digging difficult.

Generally, in Bolton at least, the measures taken to deter the resurrectionists were successful, a number of whom found their nocturnal activities disturbed by watchful Boltonians. The grave watch would be especially diligent if members of the deceased's community thought that the corpse might be of particular interest to the medical profession. One such case was reported on 20th December, 1828[5] concerning the body of a young female who had suffered from fits, the cause of which had baffled the medical profession. On the Sunday and Monday nights following her burial in the Catholic chapel, the sexton had chased off a man seen near the grave, which, on examination, suggested that someone had been trying to dig. The night watch of the young woman's grave was increased. No further disturbances were reported.

Not put off by the lack of availability of fresh corpses from the cemeteries, some resurrectionists resorted to murder. The most famous of these were the two Scots, William Burke and William Hare. When they were eventually discovered, Hare turned King's Evidence and disappeared. Burke was left to face the consequences, and was publicly hanged in Edinburgh in 1829 (Fielding, 1994). In Bolton, in June of the same year, two boys playing in a tunnel near Rose Hill, came across the body of a man wrapped in a sack. The body, in a state of high putrification, was taken to the Bridgeman's Arms to await the coroner's inquest. Several local people came forward to claim the body, including two men who said that it belonged to a late Major Robinson who had recently died when he fell off a roof. The relatives of Major

5   *Bolton Chronicle*, 20th December, 1828.

Robinson gained permission from the vicar of the cemetery in Leigh, where the deceased had been buried, to examine the grave. Robinson's body was found in the coffin.

The body was so badly decomposed that the surgeon found it impossible to determine the cause of death. He suggested it might be that of a recently deceased and buried person, who may have been disinterred by resurrectionists. However, this could not be established with any certainty. The final verdict on the body was 'deceased, found dead in a tunnel, but as how he came to be there, there is no evidence to show' (Fielding, 1994).Two years later, a Mrs. Elizabeth Hooper came to see the minister of Trinity Church. Mrs Hooper, who had been searching for her missing spouse, had been told by a man named Brewer, that the latter had been murdered near Bolton. A warrant was obtained to disinter the coffin of the unidentified man. The body was formally identified as being that of Mr Hooper and it was thus re-interred in the Trinity Churchyard (Fielding, 1994).

If the body did belong to Mr Hooper, it seems very likely that he had been murdered. Evidence as to what the motive was, or who the murderer may have been, remains a mystery. A year later, in January 1830, a man called Hannah (alias James William Hamer) was convicted at Lancaster Assizes for having in his possession, the body of a late George Dean, who had been recently buried in Bolton Parish Church graveyard (Fielding, *op cit*). Because the cause of death and the identity of the mystery body had not been established, no connection was made between its discovery and the activities of Hannah. At the time of his arrest Hannah had in his possession a series of letters that documented the somewhat fascinating progress of his 'career' as a resurrectionist. A detailed summary of these letters, 15 in all, was reported in the local paper following Hannah's conviction and sentence of six months imprisonment in Lancaster Castle.[6]

Evidence provided by these letters establishes the fact that Hannah began his career in Dublin where he started providing bodies for a Mr Fitzgerald from Edinburgh. Letter one began:

6   *Bolton Chronicle*, 6th Febuary 1830.

'My dear Hannah, attend to the above and be speedy. I shall expect to hear from you soon. You may perhaps hear a report that we have given up the Irish business but pay no attention to it.'

It seems that Hannah was having no problems in finding customers who were interested in purchasing the 'goods' of his trade. Another letter, dated 25th October, 1829 states that:

'Dr Mackenzie and the writer are all deeply interested in the business, and will take as many as he can send.'

Despite the clear demand for corpses, it seems that, in Dublin at least, Hannah was having problems. This was indicated by a later, somewhat distraught letter, from a William Hume and which implored Hannah to 'for God's sake, send something soon, for he cannot look the doctor in the face.' Despite the pleas, matters had not improved by October 26th, 1829, when another correspondence to Hannah stated the writer's:

'disappointment at not hearing from him, and informing him that classes are thronged to the door.'

In this correspondence, Hannah was urged to 'send something soon or you will frighten us all.' It seems from some of the correspondence forwarded to Hannah, that some surgeons may have been making some trade from harvesting the dead, in addition to dissection. The correspondence quoted above ends by informing him that 'Dr Askin has received an order for ten sets of teeth from a gentlemen in the country.' Hannah is asked to send these as soon as possible. It seems that Hannah's main problem with his Dublin trade was that of getting the packages containing his goods on board ships bound for Edinburgh. However, some ships' captains were more diligent than others, for the writer informs Hannah in one letter, not to worry about Captain 'O' because he would 'ship the whole population of Dublin if you choose.'

Trade in Dublin was beset with problems and, in another letter, the writer instructs Hannah to leave for Manchester 'where subjects are in great abundance.' A further letter sent following Hannah's arrival in Manchester, congratulates him for trying new ground — there's nowt like a bit of self-enterprise. The letter informs Hannah that:

> *'The doctor has frequently sent men down to Manchester who have sent up subjects (dead bodies that is) almost immediately after their arrival.'*

The writer above concludes by assuring Hannah with some optimism that he will look forward to a 'plentiful harvest.' It would seem from the letters which followed, that trade certainly picked up for Hannah once he switched his premises to the Manchester area. Indeed, his trade was becoming, what might be called, flexible, responsive to demand and competitive — all the hallmarks of a good capitalist! One of the letters from Edinburgh, informs Hannah of the activities of some Glasgow men and adds that 'their trade is a mockery compared to ours, we have dissected no less than twenty-five and the doctor has to lecture three times a day.' However, Hannah's fortunes in the north of England were short-lived. In January 1830, one of the last letters sent from Edinburgh expresses the writer's disappointment that Hannah had not sent him something for some considerable time and informing him that '25 dissections a day are not easily satisfied.'

Shortly after this correspondence, Hannah, was found in possession of the body of George Dean and arrested. The conclusion of those who investigated the case was that Hannah had obtained at least eight of the bodies he had sent on to Edinburgh, from Bolton. Body snatching, to the squeamish, seems a horrendous crime. But, there was nothing in the information, published in the Bolton Chronicle of 1830, to suggest that Hannah was guilty of anything other than stealing corpses. As stated earlier in this chapter, the death of Mr Hooper was never connected to Hannah's activities and the cause of the his death has never been established. Given the abundance of corpses Hannah did provide for the surgeons in Edinburgh, and the difficulties he must have encountered in doing so, the idea of murder may well have crossed his mind, particularly since (as some of the letters suggested) he was in a great deal of debt. It is equally probable that Hannah may well have turned a blind eye to evidence of the possibly murderous activities of some of his accomplices. Certainly, the infamous Dr Knox who received so many corpses in Edinburgh, must have ignored clear evidence of murder.

The activities of the resurrectionists ended with the passing of the 1832 Anatomy Act (Richardson, *op cit*). This Act solved the corpse shortage suffered by anatomists, with the decree that all those who died in poverty should, rather than be buried in a pauper's grave, be handed to the surgeons for dissection. This, as Richardson points out, posed a threat to the poor, which was even more worrying than the threat of the pauper's funeral. Such fears could only have increased the demand among the poor for death insurance. Richardson points out that, even today, although the threat of dissection has been removed, there is still a stigma attached to failing to make financial provision for one's funeral. It is current policy for paupers to be cremated rather than buried, and cheaper funerals are skimped and hasty affairs, often referred to by some funeral directors as the 'nine-o-clock trot.' Furthermore, it seems that fewer relatives of the deceased feel obliged to pay for the burial of family members, particularly if the latter die without any money.

In conclusion, this chapter and *Chapter 7*, has explored two social conditions — fear of the pauper's grave and fear of dissection. These have both contributed to the social and individual importance attached to funerals by working-class people. *Chapter 6* considered the role of the layer-out and the ways in which such women helped the poor to maintain some dignity in death. Having explored some of the social factors that influenced the evolution of the northern funeral, its importance, ritual and performance (for it certainly was a performance in the north), the next chapter will consider the funeral itself.

Chapter 9
A time for display:
The Bolton funeral

This chapter concludes our exploration of death rituals, funeral practices and the social conditions that influenced them. So far, we have discussed death in relation to the family, the immediate community and, more indirectly, their association with social conditions before and during the industrial revolution. We have also discussed the growth of diverse religious groups in Bolton and the impact this may have had on death rituals. In linking the public with the private, we have explored how the two can be interwoven. In this chapter we discuss the functions of funeral practices in England generally, and relate national changes to practices in the north, particularly in Bolton.

Nearly all societies have established rituals and practices for disposing of the dead. Social custom and individual preference influence methods of disposal of the bodies. The most common methods are burial and cremation. Death practices can be influenced by fear of the dead and the belief that they may come back to haunt or annoy the living. Funeral practices in some cultures, therefore, include procedures that are carried out to make the dead 'stay put'. Such practices include breaking or tying the legs or feet of the corpse and placing heavy stones either across the feet or on the grave. Religious rites frequently include actions designed to appease the dead. For example, food and water may be left at the side of the grave (Brendann, 1930). Concepts of gender appropriate behaviour also influence funeral practices. Littlewood (1993) notes that expectations of how grief should be expressed, such as wearing black clothes and social withdrawal, were imposed on women rather than men during the Victorian era. Littlewood questions whether some of the Victorian rituals might have served to control young widows. Fear that an 'irate' and jealous deceased spouse might come back to haunt the living, influence ideas about gender appropriate mourning behaviour in other cultures. Brendann described a similar belief when he wrote of the Narrinyeri in Australia:

> *'The fear attitude toward the dead finds expression among the Narrinyeri of Australia. These people believe that the souls of the deceased live in the sky, but descend at night to earth to annoy the living. Among them there is little or no trace of affection towards their departed. Although seemingly the most excessive grief is displayed which takes the form of wailing and cutting, it is the opinion of Taplin 'that fear has more to do with these exhibitions than grief', and he says that 'for one moment a woman will appear in the deepest agony of grief and tears; a few minutes after the conventional amount of weeping having been accomplished, she will laugh and talk with the merriest'. If this sorrow were not manifested, the deceased would not think that he is sufficiently mourned for, and hence would take vengeance upon the survivors.'*

Funerals apparently serve the needs of the living rather than the dead, although this point is debatable. Economic and political influences can also influence funeral practices. Advocates of the funeral argue that:

1.   Funerals provide an occasion to acknowledge the end of life for the deceased, and his or her separation from the living. Funerals provide an opportunity for the bereaved to confront the death and begin the grieving process. Although painful, this grieving process is necessary if the bereaved are to recover from the trauma of loss.

2.   Funerals constitute a 'rite of passage'. As such, they help to reaffirm the participant's belief in the immortal nature of human existence. Not all funerals are religious, since many atheist's have and attend funerals. However, atheist's have great respect for the sanctity of both life and death. Funerals have a symbolic meaning because they provide opportunities for the living to celebrate and pay tribute to, the life of the deceased.

Thus, funerals can help to maintain the emotional well-being of the individual or group.

3. Funerals are social occasions (even small, private funerals) which help to reassure and maintain the solidarity of the group. Sometimes they help to reduce family or public disharmonies which may have arisen because of a death. The deaths of President Kennedy and Dr Martin Luther King shook the world. At the time, many people reported experiencing feelings of intense grief, comparable to those which might have been expected had they lost someone they knew very well. A study conducted by Fulton in 1964, following the death of President Kennedy concluded that his funeral provided a vehicle for the expression of private as well a public grief.[1]

Critics argue that funerals can lead to exploitation of the bereaved, causing unnecessary expense, often at a time when it can be least afforded (see *Chapter 7*, pauper burials). Clearly funerals can cause disharmony, particularly if the death of the deceased increases or uncovers social frictions that existed before the death of the deceased. Social disharmony can be intensified if 'normal' funeral practices fail to be implemented or if these are disrupted in any way (Geertz, 1957). Others have argued that, since funerals act as powerful vehicles which shape our ideas about death and dying, they serve as a form of social control and political propaganda. A funeral can support both sides of the argument. In 1916 an article published in a local Bolton paper recorded that:[2]

> *'In a north midland town there were remarkable scenes on Saturday, when 10 victims of a Zeppelin raid were laid to rest in the town's cemeteries. The streets of the neighbourhood where the fatalities occurred, to the gates of the cemetery where two of the interments took place, were blocked with people long before time for the burials, and inside the funeral grounds was a tremendous crowd of people. At another cemetery there were some stirring*

---

1   From Fulton (1995).
2   *Bolton Journal and Guardian* 6th October, 1916.

scenes, for here it was that seven coffins were carried into the Catholic Church and the one Nonconformist was followed to his last resting place by 60 of his fellow workmen. Crowds of people awaited patiently from noon until 6.30 in the evening and a little rising ground was covered with a mass of people paying tribute to the unfortunate sufferers of the raid. It was not merely curiosity which drew thousands of people into the streets and open places.'

These funerals had supported the participants so that all could share the collective grief and shock. However, the funerals also provided an opportunity to raise a sense of nationalism and support for the war effort. The article continues:

'The officiating priest said that they saw how the 'brave' German soldiers fought. Here they saw how the culture and education of Germany had writ itself large upon our life today. The 'brave' soldiers had struck at the child, the mother, at the defenceless man, at everything we had been taught by the English canons of sentiment, to regard with reverence. We had been taught to defend the weak and the defenceless and to stay the hand of him who would strike. The Germans were the people who were asking us to model our education on their system. All he could say was 'God save us from the Germans.'

In the following discussion, we trace the history of the funeral from the thirteenth to the twentieth centuries.[3] Prior to this, in medieval times, the bereaved would surrender their dead to the care of the parish. Corpses of the common people were buried in open, collective graves. Removing or 'swapping around' older corpses from the mass graves were sometimes necessary to make space for new corpses. Sometimes human remains, particularly bone would be used to produce small, ornate carvings that decorated the surrounding houses. Aries' (1974) discussion of the Cemetery of the Innocents in the Paris of the Middle Ages, suggests a 'promiscuity between the living and the dead' that reflects a very different meaning of

3   Funerals during the war years are explored in Volume 2,
    A Thanatology of War.

life and death from that which is common today. In the Middle Ages, there was an acceptance of death as an end to this life and, in this context, the good death meant that the individual had to make peace with his or her maker before dying. People were less individualistic and less concerned for the welfare of the body than they were for the welfare of the soul. Coffins were very expense and few people could afford them. Corpses were transported to the grave in communal coffins.

Care of the soul of the deceased rather than the corpse was given priority during the Middle Ages and individual graves had little meaning. Interest in methods of embalming began to emerge in the late Middle Ages. When a rich person died, it was expected that a part of the deceased's body, such as the heart, should be left at the place of death as part payment for the care received. If a rich person died some distance away from home, it would be necessary to preserve the body so that it could be taken to the family. Many of the medieval priests were skilled embalmers and sometimes butchers were employed to support them. If the deceased had died some distance away from home then only the skeleton would be sent back to the family. The process of embalming the body was quite basic and involved removing all of the flesh from the body. The bones were then boiled in vinegar to ensure that they were clean of any remaining flesh. The flesh of the corpse was buried at the place of death and only the bones would be sent back to the bereaved family (Litten, 1991).

The souls of those who had only committed minor sins, went to a place called Purgatory until they had paid for their sins on earth. Payment in full of the spiritual debts incurred in life, provided admission to Heaven.

Religious masses, or chants recited for the souls of the dead could reduce the length of time they had to remain in Purgatory. Masses for the dead were chanted on four occasions following the death, with a final mass chanted on the first anniversary. These masses were extremely expensive. In addition to paying the chantry priests, costs had to cover additional items such as candles and clocks. It was considered 'good' to remember the poor so food was also provided during the mass.

As time passed, people felt it was unfair that the poor, who could not afford a mass, should have to spend longer in Purgatory than the rich. So small guilds were founded for the purpose of gathering funds to pay for collective chants for the poor. The reciting of chants for the dead died out gradually, partly because of the expense (Litten, 1991). The most significant event to contribute to the decline of the mass was the Black Death. This claimed so many lives that the expense become prohibitive, even for the rich. The Black Death may have generated early concerns for more efficient and hygienic methods of disposing of the dead. During the time of the Black Death, collective graves became so packed that the stench coming from them could be intolerable (Ziegler, 1969). Nevertheless, burial was still the preferred method of disposal until the mid nineteenth century. In the 1800s, various reformers who were concerned with public health issues, began to campaign for more hygienic methods for disposing of the dead, such as cremation.

The early advocates of cremation met with considerable opposition, mainly from religious groups who associated it with paganism. Cremation had been popular during ancient times, particularly among the Romans. Interest arose in some quarters during the eighteenth century. Some Italian scientists of the time had speculated about the design of incinerators which might lead to the development of efficient means of disposing of the dead. It was not until 1874 that the question of cremation became open to public debate. An article published in the Contemporary Review written by Sir Henry Thompson sparked the debate. Thompson had developed a very rational and scientific argument in favour of cremation. However, most bereaved people are not rational in grief and found Thompson's ideas hard to accept. Thompson's article met with considerable hostility. His argument was contested on religious grounds because it was felt that people needed the presence of the dead in order to remind them of the Christian doctrine 'Thou Shalt Die.' Objections also came from medical and legal quarters on the grounds that cremation might encourage murderers because the body could not be exhumed (Leaney, 1989).

However, despite strong opposition, cremation became acceptable, mainly due to a burial crisis at the time of the Industrial Revolution. By the mid 1800s, cemeteries were so full that the dead had to be dug up within six to twelve weeks after burial, to make room for new corpses. It was sometimes necessary to burn the remains of the exhumed corpses. So, in effect, cremations were already carried out informally in some areas. (Morley, 1971). In the nineteenth century, the middle-classes were developing a sense of revulsion at the thought of corpses rotting underground, as they increasingly associated decay with excretion. Improved standards of living may have contributed to changing attitudes. Cremation was much harder to 'sell' to the working-classes, who were still living in overcrowded conditions, with little privacy. In some instances, working-class people had to keep a corpse in the house until funds were raised to pay for a funeral. So the poor were more accustomed to the sight of the dead (Leaney, 1989).

The first case of cremation to be tested in law was that of Dr Price. Dr Price was an eccentric Welsh physician. One night his neighbours were infuriated to catch him burning the body of his late son, Jesus Christ the First on a local hill. Witnesses prevented Price from successfully completing the procedure. A struggle ensued ending with Price carrying his son's corpse back home. Price placed the corpse under his bed where it stayed until his arrest three days later when, provoked by what they had seen, the local people decided to prosecute. Price was brought to trial at Cardiff but to the further indignation of the people, the judge, Dr Justice Stephen decreed that:

> '*a person who burns, instead of burying, a dead body does not commit a criminal act unless he does it in a such manner as to amount to a public nuisance at common law*' *and* '*that to burn a body decently and inoffensively is lawful, at least not criminal*'

> (cited by Leaney, 1989).

Following this case, advocates of cremation campaigned to have cremation legitimised and regulated by law. The Disposal of the Dead Regulation Bill was passed in 1885 after which preference for cremation grew rapidly (Leaney, *op cit*). However, this national change in attitude was not reflected in Bolton. Here burial remained the popular method of disposal of the dead until the mid 1970s. In the 1970s, Bolton's crematorium held an open day to dispel some of the public's fears about cremation. The leaflet distributed to promote the open day, showed romantic images of the Gardens of Remembrance accompanied by extracts from Shakespeare's verses, sometimes with amusing consequences:

> *'We are such stuff as dreams are made on,*
> *And our little lucks are rounded with a sleep'*
> *Shakespeare Hamlet — (whoops) — the Tempest!'*

Romantic descriptions of various features of the crematorium such as the Book of Remembrance which:

> *'Consists of four beautifully bound volumes, one to each quarter of the year, and the leaves are of the finest vellum. The book is on view daily, under a glass canopy and in full view on each anniversary of a passing from this life.'*

Overdale Crematorium is very beautiful and cremation at the time of writing has become very popular in the town. Given the strength of the influence of the many religious groups in the town, one can only speculate as to why burial remained the preferred method of disposing of the dead for so long. It is true that since the late 1800s, sympathy for the cremation movement has grown, even in many religious quarters as the following article in a local newspaper suggests:[4]

> *'The Dean of York, chairman of the church of England Burial Reform Association, speaking at a meeting held at the Mansion House, York, under the presidency of the Lord Major, said that it was absurd to call cremation hostile to Christianity. If it were so what could be said of the martyrs who were burned to death. Whether burning or burial was to be the practice of the future, was a question for scientific men, who do not yet seem to have made up their minds.'*

4   *Bolton Guardian*, 4th November, 1887.

The extract above is interesting, not just because it reflects changing attitudes of the church towards cremation, but also towards science and medicine. In the early days of the Enlightenment and indeed, well into the mid 1800s, science and the church had made uncomfortable bedfellows in matters relating to death and dying. By the late 1800s, some members of the church had virtually surrendered this authority to the men of science. Despite this surrender, it is clear from the article that the responsibility for maintaining the spiritual integrity of the dead still rested with the church. The Dean of York continues:

> *'Their own duty as members of the Burial Reform Association was clear. On the one hand they must avoid the contempt of the body shown in huddling it with other bodies in the same grave.'*

In Bolton, since the mid 1800s, there has been an increase in the importance attached to the social and spiritual significance of the funeral. Laungani (1997) has drawn our attention to the fact that the modern crematorium can make the bereaved feel alienated. This can happen even for Hindus for whom cremation has always been the preferred method of disposal. Until very recent years, services held in crematoriums have had a clinical atmosphere to them, which can be off putting to both the religious and atheists. Given the public display that has been so traditional in Bolton funerals, it is hardly surprising that cremation took so long to become popular.

Before the demise of the textile industry, the town managed to retain a sense of community spirit and continuity with previous generations. Even at the present time, it is not unusual for people to have a grave site, already occupied with late members of the family, and with space for those who are still alive. To many older (and indeed some younger) local people, thoughts of burial in the same place as one's ancestors in the local cemetery are not in the least 'off putting'. Some people prepare for this eventuality when still young. One of the authors, for example, has many of her late relatives buried in Astley Bridge Cemetery. They had chosen and purchased the grave site while they were still quite young. The author's late maternal grandparents and great aunt and uncle purchased a grave for four, when they were in their early thirties. The rationale for the location of the site chosen was that the grave occupants would still be able to feel the sun coming up every morning. Other people interviewed spoke of the dead keeping each other company and even talking to each other from the grave. As one woman (aged 45 years at the time of the interview in 1995) put it:

> *'I want to be buried with my husband, then I can talk to him forever, and nag him to death if I want to, forever and ever (laughs)... and so that we can keep each other company. I couldn't even think of cremation, because if I were cremated, well then how could I be sure that I'd be next to my husband, I mean your ashes can get all over the place can't they? Anyway, all the women of the family are buried in Astley Bridge Cemetery. So I'll never be lonely' because I can talk to them even if he doesn't want to talk ... in fact, if he doesn't behave himself, he'll get nagged by the lot of us (laughs) and just imagine, there'll be no escape.'*

Much of the conversation above was said in jest but it reflects a strong belief in an afterlife. The woman quoted above is a Catholic and, unlike other religions, the Pope has only given his approval to cremation in recent years. The younger Catholics interviewed expressed a preference in the event of their own death, for cremation. The older people interviewed (aged forty upwards) expressed a strong belief in the continuation of life (and indeed, sensation) after death. Religious faith expressed by some of the older people interviewed was very strong, even in those who did not attend church regularly. There was a certain vanity in the attitude of some which seemed a little at odds with Christian thinking. If we turn back to the article recorded in the Bolton Chronicle in 1885 for example, the Dean of York concluded his discussion on burial by stating that:

> *'On the other hand, they (ie. members of the burial association) must guard against the worship of the body shown in preserving it in solid coffin and vault.'*

In other words, the Dean was concerned about a growing individualism in people's attitudes towards death, which contradicts Christian thinking far more than cremation ever did. If an individual really believes in an afterlife in heaven, why on earth worry about preserving the body after death? Despite this apparent contradiction, the funeral has been increasingly commercialised since the Elizabethan period. The Elizabethan age was one of prosperity, at least for the rich, so many could afford their own coffins. It was during this period that the funeral became a status symbol. After all, having one's remains stored in a tailor-made coffin, reflects a concern for individual privacy and a degree of materialism. It is a common saying that we cannot take wealth with us, that 'shrouds do not have pockets.' The desire for an expensive funeral suggests an attempt (albeit perhaps at an unconscious level) to do just that — to take it all, or at least as much as you can, with you. It is difficult to say how common was the demand and practice of burying people in this individualistic way in the north at the time of Elizabeth I. Reference is made in Ainsworth (1995) to the tombs and graves of the better off. However, it is important to remember that this was a novel written in the late nineteenth century, by which time individual graves and extravagant funeral practices had become quite common. Although very well written, it is fair to say that the author took a degree of poetic licence. So the book does not paint a completely accurate picture of the times of the Lancashire witches. However, the north had its wealthy, just like everywhere else, so it can be assumed that extravagant funerals were becoming popular and available, at least for the better off.

Initially, the individualised funeral was a status symbol which only the wealthier people could afford. It did not take merchants long to see that there was a gap in the market that could prove quite lucrative. Despite the high rates of poverty during the Industrial Revolution, people often had extravagant and 'respectable' funerals for their dead by the 1840s. Various references were made in newspaper reports of the time, to individual graves and coffins. However, the coffins purchased by many poor families were very flimsy and 'body snatching' was easy (see *Chapter 8*). By the 1840s, a strict code of conduct associated with the funeral had evolved and if it was violated, it caused public outrage and even aggression.

A report published in one local paper during the 1832 cholera outbreak, provides some insight into the strength of feeling that typified funerals at the time:[5]

> *'Rev Mr Airey, officiating minister at our parish church, having been apprised that the three cases mentioned were those of the deceased cholera victims, he fixed the time for interring the bodies at 5 o'clock on Thursday afternoon and agreeably with the order of the Bishop of the diocese intended to read the funeral service over them, without permitting the remains to be taken into the church. The whole of the funerals were at the church exactly at 6 o'clock, the usual time of internment at this season of the year, and a large crowd of persons were assembled at the entrance into the church yard, who demanded that the bodies should be taken into the church. The people from Harwood were prevailed upon to move away from the entrance of the church, but the attendants of the funeral of Annie Chadwick forced the corpse into the aisle in spite of pleas from the clergyman, the sexton and clerk, and the funeral was performed in the usual manner.'*

The above suggests that some lay people had a greater concern for the spiritual well-being of the dead than for the health of the living. It also infers a class struggle that attaches more importance to the people than to religion. The Reverend Airy was an educated man and was clearly concerned to remove the threat to the health and safety of the living that the corpse posed. This was a reasonable concern given that cholera is very contagious. The reader will note that the article refers to the corpse of the deceased rather than the coffin. The expense of funerals and related accessories, such as coffins, were beyond the means of many working-class people. Without the confinement of a coffin, the corpse may well have posed a greater threat to the living than it might otherwise have done. Reverend Airy was overruled on this occasion because of ordinary people's concern for the dead. There are several

5   *Bolton Chronicle*, 1st September, 1832.

issues, pertinent at the time, which may have influenced the course of the events described above. The first was the increasing importance of funerals as status symbols. In the 1800s the perceived importance of a 'decent' funeral was present in all classes of society. For the poor, provision of as 'decent' a funeral as the family could afford, provided a public statement to the effect that they were not paupers. Reverend Airy's attempts to modify the service, compromised the bereaved family's concern to present a public show of respectably.

Religions have different meanings to different people. Levels of education can shape such meanings in complex ways. While education may have no bearing on the depth of faith experienced by a believer, it may influence the degree of flexibility readers allow in their interpretations of the bible. The Reverend Airy may have interpreted the bible with greater flexibility because he studied it from a theoretical perspective. This would inevitably lead to greater flexibility of practice. We can infer that the family of Annie Chadwick were quite poor because they could not afford a coffin. The bereaved family may have interpreted the bible from a more pragmatic perspective. A pragmatic perspective can lead to more a rigid interpretation of a source. This is because people use a pragmatic perspective when they want some practical guidelines on how to conduct their lives. Such differences are unlikely to have influenced the day-to-day relationship the clergy shared with the people of the parish. Because a funeral is so emotive, such differences would have greater importance.

Disagreements about funeral practices can arise between people from different denominations. Attitudes towards Catholic funerals appear to have been quite negative during the 1800s and may have reflected some of the racism directed at the Irish at that time. Newspaper reports suggest that the Irish wake, in particular, appears to have been a sore point for non-Catholics.[6]

> '*Mr Barrow of the Joiners Arms, Deansgate was charged with having company in his house on Sunday 16th*

---

6   *Bolton Chronicle*, 12th November, 1831.

October, during the hours of divine service. It appeared that the information was laid by Mr Barrett, by order of the Boroughreeve and Constables, and the facts as stated by Rollingson were that when he went into the house, there was a large body of drunken men in, and Mr Barrow's men were trying to get them out. He did not see any drinking going on. The company were chiefly Irish. Mr Barrow said that he had not filled any liquors for his customers after 2 o'clock, and had been from that time to the constables coming in, mainly endeavouring to get rid of them. They were not drunk, as had been stated, for they had not had sufficient to make them so. He had several of them in attendance to prove that he had refused to fill them a single drop after 2 o'clock.

It is difficult to judge the truth of the publican's evidence. The problem of 'after time' drinking was one that the founders of the temperance movement were keen to address. There are also contradictions in the statements recorded. On the one hand the publican insists that the men were not drunk. On the other he is reported to have said:

'The fact was that they (the drunken men) had been to an Irish funeral, and as customary, had merely called to drink the peace to the deceased. They might you know have had something to drink before they went to the chapel, certainly they might. Mr Barrett said that Irish funerals were productive of great disturbance in the town, as the friends, relatives, countrymen and all connected with the deceased, thought nothing in this blessed world, as soon as the breath was out of the body, but of eating, drinking and kicking up rows.'

The obvious racism implied did not go unchallenged and an Irish person responded to Barrett's claims by:

'Ejaculating something very much like a passage in one of the hymns of the 'unknown tongue' ... but we are assured that this was 'real Irish' and being freely translated, meant that Mr Barrett was rather embellishing the facts.'

Barrett was not charged, despite the fact that that he had been accused of the same offence on several occasions. By seizing hold of a stereotype, Barrett managed to explain away the fact that he had broken the law. This does not mean that Barrett was necessarily a racist. Rather, he was able to use racist feelings and beliefs which were dominant at the time, to his own advantage. Wakes had always distressed the sanctimonious, as suggested by the following letter written to the editor of a local paper.[7] The writer with some indignation states that:

> 'Sir — I have no hesitation in stating in the most deliberate manner, that there is nothing which is in any degree, so generally and practically injurious to the minds, morals and habits of the population, and consequently to the peace, order and happiness of the community as the Wakes which are held in the neighbourhood.'

He argues that participants of wakes, 'walked in the counsel of the ungodly' participating in them 'with the full intention of becoming intoxicated', and continues with 'all of the scriptures joined together consider revelling and drunkenness as amongst those works of the flesh that shut men out from the Kingdom of God.' We can be confident that those who think drink will 'shut one out from the Kingdom of God' will be unimpressed with a custom of seeing the dead out by becoming intoxicated. Despite disapproval in some areas, the Irish wake had become quite a feature of the town by the mid 1800s and as time went by, people developed greater tolerance. Indeed, many of those interviewed looked on the wake with approval. Wakes had become a source of local pride by the 1950s and many people had vivid recollections of them:

> 'Oh they were quite something the Irish Wakes, why, I've been told that way back, they used to open the coffin up and stand it up. So the corpse would be like, standing there in the coffin looking at them all. But it didn't bother them, why they'd get chairs and then they would all sit round and talk to it, they'd even toast it, and tell it jokes...

7   *Bolton Chronicle*, 8th September, 1827.

*oh yes, it was quite an event, an Irish Wake. But it wasn't
a sad event, it was like a tribute to the dead person, a way
of saying, well here's to a life well lived. I suppose it was
also a way of coming to terms with the death really, for
the family and of course, you couldn't really avoid
thinking about your own death could you? Not with a
corpse stood there. But the thing is, people didn't just talk
in a meaningless way to the corpse. They would
remember experiences they had shared with that person
when they were alive. And some of those experiences
could be quite funny, in which case of course people
would laugh. But the thing is, I think that hearing people
talk about those memories could be a comfort to the
family, because it was a way of summing up, if you see
what I mean kind of, this person had a real impact on
peoples lives, I think that that was the main advantage of
a wake more then any other kind of funeral. People joke
about an Irish Wake, they see it as a free for all, just an
excuse for getting drunk ...but there was much more to it
than that.'*

A man in his early sixties, assured the interviewer that
toasting the dead in England was not half as enjoyable as it
had once been in Northern Ireland. This was due to the fact
that it had once been customary in some parts, to take the
coffin into the local pub and hold the wake there. This
interviewee remembered the very first wake he attended
when, as a boy, he had lived in Northern Ireland:

*'There were these men who were related to the man who
had died, and they had come down from the hills for the
funeral. They wore big black hats, with a big rim and
they looked really impressive and they had big long
beards, I think. I didn't know them, I'd never seen them
before, but apparently they were related and so came
along ...in the pub, for each round, you buy a pint or
whatever, for the deceased and then you place it on the
coffin. So by the end of the wake, the coffin lid would be
full of glasses... and the glasses were full, and the thing
is, well he (the deceased) couldn't drink them could he?
So everyone would be pissed, even the publican and his*

staff... waste not, want not! You don't get wakes like that in England! I don't know, you might not get them there anymore.'

The man quoted above had settled in Bolton many years ago and had not visited Northern Ireland for some time. Another man interviewed in his mid forties and also from Northern Ireland, assured the interviewer that funeral wakes were still a very strong feature of the culture:

'Yes, in Northern Ireland, if you die on Monday, you are buried on Wednesday. So on Monday night the body comes home, you have the wake. Then on Tuesday evening the body goes to church, it is submitted to the church for overnight, and we have the mass. Being Roman Catholic, we have mass, and then you go to the graveside and say the prayers at the graveside. But here (on the mainland) we can have bodies here for weeks and weeks at a time, no one cares you know. I mean, in Northern Ireland you would not get a situation like we have here, where a body can be left in the mortuary for weeks, and for someone to say 'oh well we won't bother to make any funeral arrangements now, we are off on holiday now so we'll arrange for the funeral when we get back.'

Regardless of religious affiliation, the funeral in Bolton, has remained very important. How much it may change in the years to come is open to speculation. Other researchers have noted the importance of funerals in the north. An observer who took part in the Mass Observation Study 1937, wrote of the Bolton funeral that 'according to the fierce code of conduct in the area, this is a time for display.'

A recent collection of Humphrey Spender's photographs taken during the Study reflects how important funerals were during the 1930s.[8] The photographs depict the funeral of a late John Shaw. The street's images captured in the photographs and the clothing of the mourners, suggest that Shaw may have been a person of moderate means. However, there are still two

8   Spender H (1995) *Work Town People: Photographs From Northern England.*

and possibly three black cars captured in the image. It was probably quite an expense for the family at the time to pay for so many cars. The roof of the funeral car is covered with flowers. This suggests some financial generosity on the part of the mourners, given that the photograph was taken at a time when wages were quite low. The funeral appears to have been well attended. Spender noted that, 'Most of the men had tears in their eyes; one or two had obviously been weeping previous to the funeral.' At least ten people who did not form part of the funeral procession stood near at the cemetery during the service at the graveside. There is also a photograph in the collection of two women who peeped at the procession from behind a nearby gravestone. The photographs are valuable sources of local history. They provide further evidence that funerals in Bolton had been very public affairs in the past. One woman interviewed recalled, the social practices observed by the community during a funeral in the mid fifties:

'When the funeral car drew up, the family would join the hearse. If possible the family would be in black cars too, if they could afford it. The cars would have to drive quite slow to the cemetery. If it was quite near, then people who knew the dead person might join the procession as it passed the house. So, as the funeral went along, you would see all these doors opening and people would either stand at the door, or join the procession. So you'd have this line of people walking behind, and it would be growing longer as it went along. Even if people didn't join the procession, it was expected that everyone in the street should close their curtains when there was a death, at least on the day of the funeral. If they didn't do that then people would call them fit to burn ... oh, you know, they'd say 'fancy that, such and such a body never closed their curtains, how mean' you would hear them say. I remember once, there was a new driver (of the hearse) he must have been new, because he didn't know that he was supposed to drive slow. Well it was funny. People were joining the procession, and they had to walk fast, then they had to trot, then they had to run like ... very fast (laughs). Well the poor sods were beggared by the time they got to the cemetery. They were puffing and panting

*and sweat was rolling down their faces. Oh it was funny
and of course, no one complained, well they did under
their breath like 'the bloody idiot' meaning the driver,
and all this. But it was all under your breath like because
it was a funeral, so you had to be ever so respectable.'*

Humour came up quite a lot in the transcripts. A married
couple interviewed remembered that a late relative had given
strict instructions prior to his death, that there should be
black cars provided for all mourners who attended his funeral.
The rationale — he did not want a carnival following him. In
the nineteenth century communal graves were provided for
those too poor to afford a funeral. A child death did not appear
to have the same social significance that it might have today,
perhaps due to high mortality rates. In her book on death
rituals in Preston, Roberts (1989) writes of an interviewee,
who as a young girl, placed the body of her stillborn sibling in a
local pauper grave. A similar story was published in a Bolton
paper in 1846.[9] This records the case of a single woman who
gave birth to a child who died within a few days of the delivery.
The mother asked a neighbour to take the child to the priest at
the Catholic chapel to be baptised. The neighbour obliged, but
the child died as she carried it home. The mother explained to
her neighbour that she had no money to bury her child. So the
neighbour and a friend put the child's body in a box and took it
back to the Catholic chapel. Unable to find the grave digger,
one of the women 'lifted a plank under which there were a
great many coffins and put the box in'. The case caused
something of a stir because the women had not told anyone
what they had done.

When the priest enquired about the child he had
baptised the day before, he found out about the death and the
rather casual burial. The priest decided to investigate. He
found the box containing the body of the child in the
communal grave and opened it. The priest found a bruise on
the forehead of the dead child so he reported the incident to
the police and an inquest was held. At the inquest the sexton
explained that the communal grave used by the women was

9   937–38, Mulford J, ed. Falling House Press, Bristol,
     Bolton Free Press, 16th December, 1846.

provided for those who could not afford to bury their dead. He also explained that communal graves were usually covered by a plank of wood, until full. Clearly access to the communal graves must have been very easy. The woman who buried the child knew exactly where to go and exactly what to do. So she may have used the grave before for a similar purpose.

Witnesses to the birth of the child, testified that the bruise was present at birth. Neighbours described the mother as 'a steadfast, decent and clean woman'. The verdict recorded was 'death by natural causes' and the coroner cautioned the two women who had disposed of the box 'against burying children in this way'. The case suggests that it may have been common practice to place the bodies of children in an open grave, sometimes without telling anyone.

At the time of writing, funerals are still quite social events in some areas of Bolton, although practices are changing and diversifying. This appears to be the case generally as society becomes more cosmopolitan, with increasing numbers of people living what might once have been considered 'unconventional' lives. Below we include an extract from Cant (1997) writing of the funeral of Linda Ngcobo in Soweto in 1993:

> *'He (Ngcobo) had been a founder member of the Gay and Lesbian Organisation of Witwatersrand (GLOW) and the organiser of the Miss GLOW annual drag show while still maintaining good relations with his actively Christian family. The funeral was addressed by both the gay ANC activist, Simon Nkoli, calling for tolerance and equal rights and by a preacher denouncing the sins of the flesh. The Glow barrier was unfolded over the coffin and members of GLOW, some in drag, paraded up the aisle to the amazement of the respectably clad Christians in white suits. It may not have been a peaceful funeral but it was an acknowledgement of the fact that Ncgobo had come from a traditional African Christian community, but had lived his adult life in a radical Gay community; they had both been part of his life and there was a place for both of them at his funeral.'*

In areas such as Halliwell and Astley Bridge, people often hold a kind of modified Irish wake. People meet and reminiscence about experiences they shared with the deceased when he or she was still alive. These conversations usually take place in the local pub following the funeral service. This does not happen so frequently in bigger cities according to the employee of a mortuary who was interviewed:

'People say, 'well how do you cope with all these grieving people and all these relatives crying all over the place?' But I would say that out of every hundred deaths, you probably get about 10%, maybe even less then 10% of these who are actually grieving. The majority who come in here, its 'right, where's the money, where's the key to the flat?' you know what I mean, and the majority are not interested. As long as there's enough money to pay for the funeral, and it doesn't cost them anything, and as long as there are possessions in that flat that they can take or sell, that's all they are interested in. And here again, we get about 90 decomposed bodies a year, which is fairly high because you do have a lot of bed sits and a lot of one roomed accommodation. They can die and be laying there for weeks and weeks before the neighbours realise that something is wrong, until the smell hits them. They realise you know that there's a funny smell coming from out of the flat. Its just the way things are going, things are very fragmented now. You do think about the situation, but you don't feel sorry for the person as such, because most have died a natural death, just passed away in their sleep, which is what most of us want anyway'.

A good quality coffin is considered the centre piece of a good funeral even today. We have already discussed the Dean of York's concern about the importance attached to expensive coffins. His concern for the issue appears to have been ignored and its significance and importance has grown over the years. In the interview material gathered for the purposes of this study, there was much discussion about the importance of a good coffin.

The preferred type for five of the women interviewed, was a 'good solid oak coffin that won't let in the air.' There was much disappointment expressed by one woman when she was told that oak coffins were no longer available. So if the importance of respectable funerals had become well established, at least in older people, by the mid twentieth century, then the coffin appears to have been, and still is, the cornerstone of that status symbol. Coffins are one of the main features in any funeral directors catalogue of goods. Expertise in their design and production has come a long way from Elizabethan times when they were a luxury for the privileged few. The production of coffins was the main concern of the early sixteenth century funeral guilds. Merchants attached to the guilds made other types of furnishing and did not concern themselves with the provision of a service for the bereaved. It was not until the nineteenth century that funeral directors were established as a professional group in their own right. The British Institute of Undertakers was established in 1898. This was reformed in 1935, becoming the National Association of Funeral Directors. The British Organisation of Funeral Directors was founded in 1982. Its aims were to improve the knowledge and practice of the profession in order to maintain and improve the quality of the service (Litten, 1991). More recently, the National Funerals College has been established. The aim of the college is to bring together various professional groups to see how improvements in the service can be made. The college also runs short courses to bring together local clergy, funeral directors, crematorium managers and other bereavement services to open up a dialogue of what can be done locally (Young, 1996).

If a death takes place in hospital, or unexpectedly in the community, then the corpse is taken to the mortuary. This is usually so that a post-mortem can be carried out. Morticians and funeral directors have come in for quite a lot of criticism. Popularity amongst the middle-classes for extravagant funerals reached a peak during the Victorian era, and then declined as commentators of the time, such as Dickens, become increasingly critical. As the middle-classes tried to simplify the funeral, the working-classes began to value an expensive and lavish 'send off.' However, this book attempts to present a balanced view of all of the issues discussed. We hope to show that the professionals who now deal with death, have an important role to play. Many take this role very seriously. The author who interviewed employees of a London hospital morgue was very impressed with the sensitivity and caring attitude of the staff. For example, the Director of Forensic Pathology when interviewed remarked that:

> 'Well I always taught my staff to treat the bodies with respect and remind them that this is someone's mother, or father or son, or whatever, and so to treat them in the way that you would want someone who belongs to you to be treated, and its, well there's no other way of doing it, I mean, they are a person. The fact that they are dead doesn't make them less so. And that body has rights, just like a living person, it has the right to be treated with respect.'

The mortuary visited was very busy and this raises questions about whether those who work with the dead have adequate support and recognition for their work. Below is one of the interviewees summary of their daily activities:

> 'We have about 15,000 deaths a year coming through here, that's just this mortuary alone, and about 46% are for actual post-mortem. Now out of 46%, 96% of that is actually for the coroner, this is where the death is either sudden death, suicides, homicides,

And the list of duties went on and on, suggesting that the emotional stain on employees, even in a relatively well staffed mortuary, must be very great. The speaker adopted a noticeably detached tone as he gave the above details. When asked about handling stressful situations, humour was the main coping strategy reported. The medical and clinical elements of the work were apparent, particularly in a society, such as ours, that associates professionalism with the cold rationality of science. But the interviewees also expressed a very sensitive and humanistic attitude towards the bereaved. The mortuary's relatives liaison officer for example, stressed the importance of listening and adopting an open, non-judgmental approach when dealing with the bereaved. In the quotation below she speaks of her experience of supporting bereaved mothers:

'seeing a mother holding her (dead) baby, dressing her baby, knowing that, I mean I'm a mum myself, and I know that some say, well what's worse, a miscarriage in the early stages, or a still birth, some say a miscarriage because you never get to see the baby, some say a still birth, but as for which one is worse, if you have never been there how can you know? Speaking for myself, I couldn't cope with going through nine months with nothing at the end to show for it. So to me that is the hardest for me to have to deal with, a mother, to be there while she holds her baby, and she is holding it for the last time, and to just be there, just rubbing her back and being with her while she holds that baby for the last time, that for me is the hardest.'

Despite the obvious emotional hardship posed by her job, the interviewee reported high levels of job satisfaction. The use of humour was also adopted by the team to help them to cope with difficult situations. This is discussed further in *Chapter 10*. It is sufficient to end this chapter with an appeal that those who work with the dead, in their various employment capacities, get the credit they deserve.

We hope in concluding this chapter, that we have promoted a largely positive image of the professionals who deal with death, recognising the value of the work they do.

On Wednesday, April 2nd 1997 the following letter appeared in the Daily Mirror Newspaper:

> *'I hope the Tories don't get in at the coming election. They've managed to get rid of two million unemployed with their Job Seekers Allowance. They might try to get rid of a similar number of pensioners with a Grave Seekers Allowance'.*

The letter above provides us with a mild example of, what Freud called, 'Gallows Humour' that is, humour connected with death. People draw death into all aspects of life, indicating that our awareness of our own individual mortality is something that we carry with us, albeit at an unconscious level, most of the time. We sometimes express this knowledge of our mortality by making jokes about death. Gallows humour seems to be most common in situations where an individual's imminent death seems certain or at least very likely. A colleague of one of the authors had served in the Gulf War. He told her that those who served in the Gulf would often ask 'has anyone got a book I can borrow, a short one!' A woman interviewed spoke of how her mother was always trying to pursuade the father to go out for a walk for his health. The scenario below describes how the father fed up with the daily 'nagging' retaliated one day:

> *'Tha keeps on telling me I should go out for me health, well let me tell thi', Mr Brown went up Moss Bank ... ee's art! Mr Bradley went up Rivington ... ee's art!*
> *And poor old Mr Black..........ee goes art o back privy for a shite ... next thing, poor old bugger ... ee's art! So if thi' don't mind I'll sit er in front o fire, cos I don't want ter be the next who's art!* [1]

1   The men discussed by the father had all 'dropped dead' of a heart attack while out of the house. Poor Mr Black was found dead sitting on the outside lavatory.

Contemporary health issues at any point in time can sometimes become mingled with gallows humour. A woman interviewed spoke of a report published in the 1950s, which suggested that the lead used in newspaper print might be carcinogenic.[2] Having read the report, the woman's father decided it was high time he persuaded his thrifty spouse to buy 'proper' toilet paper. The following transcript material describes the scene:

> *'I always felt quite superior about the fact that our family were one of the first in the street to use proper toilet paper. That's because my dad got a bee in his bonnet about lead causing cancer. He had read that the lead in newspaper could cause cancer like. So he decided to tackle my mother about it. We were sitting at the tea table, and dad said, 'I say Lizzy they say that newspapers might be causing cancer'. I've been thinking maybe we should heed the warning like and buy some proper toilet paper'. Well my mother wasn't very keen because toilet paper seemed quite expensive then, you know. You were posh if you could afford proper toilet paper. Plus I think she enjoyed cutting the newspaper up. She took great pride in cutting it into nice sized sheets and then she stuck these sheets on a nail, all neat like, in the outside loo. So she was humming and highing about this. Well my dad got really exasperated with her and he said 'listen woman, I say we'll have proper toilet paper from now on — cos I'm not wiping cancer on my arse!'*

Learning to cope with our own mortality is probably one of most difficult tasks we have to deal with in life. The experience of bereavement is painful, not just because it involves the loss of someone for whom we love or care, it also reminds us of our own mortality. Two of the individuals interviewed for the book, both employees in a mortuary explained that one of the most difficult aspects of the job was that it reminds one constantly of one's own mortality:

2   Newspaper was used as lavatory paper by many households of the time.

Interviewee 1: 'maybe its a case of getting older, and you really start thinking along those lines, I'm forty-two now, and there's lots of people coming in about my age, and you look at that and start to see parallels, I mean, death doesn't frighten me, no I'm not worried about death, its more the way that I'm going to die that worries me more than anything else, but it is true that you are confronted with it, I mean, that's the one thing we are all sure of from the day we are born, we are all going to die.'

Interviewee 2: 'Well yes, I'm thirty-two, and at that age you usually get people coming in, and mostly its something like drugs or something like that which has caused their death. But since I came here I've looked at death in a very different way. I used to be frightened of the word death and of anything to do with death. I used to be oh no! no! no! I didn't want anything to do with death. But after starting to work here I've started to think, well death is a fact. You know that you are going to face it someday. How can you avoid knowing that when you face it here every day? So now death is just death.'

The people interviewed, who worked in a mortuary, reported that humour was the most useful strategy for helping them to deal with difficult situations. Thinking about our own mortality is unpleasant. In the past, people were forced to confront death because it was so much a part of life. Professionals now deal with the dead and we are no longer exposed to this confrontation. The impact of bereavement is anaesthetised, almost to the point that it has become a taboo subject (Aries, 1974). Despite our modern attitudes, we cannot hide from death all through our life. Laughter in situations where we have to confront death replaces the unpleasant with pleasant feelings.

We do not always express gallows humour at the time of a death. It may occur many years after when people reflect on the situation and see aspects of it that, although not at all funny at the time, later provide a source of amusement. The mother of one of the authors spoke of the death of one of her late aunts, which caused the family great anguish. This was not due to the death of the aunt, although she was greatly loved and respected but she had lived to a great age and her death had been anticipated. But the hospital lost her dentures. The distress this caused the family was quite profound because it meant that the deceased had to be buried in a very 'undignified' state. The missing teeth also proved an intolerable source of embarrassment to the family. The aunt died at a time when it was customary for neighbours to call and view the body of the deceased. The story passed on into the family's oral history. Other witnesses to the event, told the author that the aunt's toothless corpse presented a pretty hideous sight — definitely not for the squeamish. But years later, people could see the funny side of the story and the author's mother commemorated it in the following poem:

The Lost Teeth

Nobody snuffed it, when I was a child,
They passed over, or slept, but they never died.
My Aunt passed on in a hospital bed
Where they lost her false teeth, so the nurses all said.

She had a twin sister, my old Aunt Jane,
Who brought the late aunty back, at her home to be laid.
She lay there all pristine and neat in her bed.
There she slept till the funeral — but never was dead.

Aunt Jane was upset by the loss of the teeth,
For seeing her, toothless, expanded her grief.
So she pleaded and begged that the hospital look,
For aunt's false teeth in each cranny and nook.

The neighbours came daily to pay their respect
But, as they gazed at her, said 'oh dear me, what next?'
They couldn't believe that the hospital staff
Could ever have made such an almighty gaff.

Where could they have lost them? One even said
'I'll bet they're now planted in some other head'.
Maybe a poor patient with no teeth at all
Woke up one morning to find Auntie's installed.

We said a few prayers as in the coffin she lay
And after each amen, all heard Auntie Jane say

'Its a pity the false teeth never got found
For now its too late she'll be soon in the ground.'

On the road to the graveyard, Aunt Jane carried on
The teeth seemed to fret her more than Auntie, who'd gone.
Maybe she thought, Peter would lock heavens gate
At the sight of poor Auntie in her toothless state.[3]

(Joan Miller, work in progress.)

Gallows humour typically appears to be 'sick' or insensitive if taken out of context. The problem with humour is that it is very contextual. In other words, it makes little sense to people who were not present in the situation in which it occurs, so that misunderstandings can arise. An American journal published an anonymous paper written by a casualty nurse. The nurse wrote that:

> *'It is no secret that hospital people frequently seem to enjoy warped humour, not always of the most loveable kind. Richard Hooker dramatised this in MASH, where burned patients became 'Crispy Critters' and Vietnam casualties were 'Jungle Burgers.'*

(Anonymous paper, 1985)

The writer continues by explaining that hospital workers frequently laugh because they do care. Confronting suffering and death as frequently as they do, causes them to develop strategies to help them cope. As the writer states 'we need a balance of joy to counteract the sorrow'. The writer points out that 'Being human and being clumsy jugglers, we will sooner or later laugh at the wrong time'. The writer continues his paper by describing an occasion when, following a cardiac arrest in which the patient died, he offended a member of the bereaved family who had heard him joking about the situation. The writer appeals to the reader to understand that jokes made in such situations do not indicate any lack of respect. These are merely reactions to a highly charged situation.

---

3   The name of the Aunt mentioned in the poem has been changed.

At the present time, it is mainly the caring professionals who deal with death, so gallows humour is more likely to be encountered in a health care situation. Gallows humour was much more common among the public in the past. This is because, as Spiegl (1971) writes:

> *'Our ancestors had to learn to live in close proximity with death. They looked on him as a friend and like any good friend, expected him to take banter in good part.'*

If we are to engage in a discussion about any kind of humour, it first needs to be defined. Hillman (1994) writes that this in itself can be as difficult as attempting to find a universal language. The spontaneous and situational nature of humour makes it very difficult to define. Spontaneous humour is often manifest by a witty remark inspired by the circumstances at hand. The success of a joke, depends not only on the skills of the person who made it, but on those who hear it. What is witty to one group of people, might not be witty in another context with different people. Gliner (1986) considers humour to be 'that quality which appeals to the sense of the ridiculous or absurdly incongruous'. Sometimes gallows humour can be used to convey quite serious social and political messages — a case of 'many a truth spoke in jest'? The following inscription, cited in Spiegl's book on gravestone humour, makes a political statement about the state of sanitation in the town because the grave occupants were:

> *'All victims of the neglect of sanitary regulation and specifically referred to in a recent lecture in this town.'*[4]

Chapter 1 described the case of a man who had died when he fell into a midden stead. It would seem from the inscription below that midden steeds were quite dangerous and had caused several deaths:

---

4   This was taken from a gravestone in Sutton. The deaths caused a celebrated law case (Spiegl 1971).

> *'Here layette the body of Martin Hyde*
> *He fell down a midden and grievously died*
> *James Hyde his brother*
> *fell down another*
> *They now lie interred side by side'*

The inscription above has entered English folklore with the limerick:

> *There was an old fellow from Hyde*
> *Who fell down a closet and died*
> *He had a young brother*
> *Who fell down another*
> *And now they're interred side by side*[5]

A number of authors have attempted to define humour and to evaluate the therapeutic value it may have. Raskin (1985) identifies three theoretical positions in psychology. These include disparagement-related theories, release-related theories and incongruity-related theories. We will discuss each of these theories in relation to death.

Disparagement-related theories are influenced by the work of the English philosopher, Thomas Hobbies. The underpinning rationale is that humour is an expression of human aggression, and that the function of jokes is to denigrate the audience or third party. There are two perspectives of the value of humour within this rationale. The first is that humour is valuable because it provides a civilised outlet for violence and aggression, which might otherwise be expressed as an act of combat. The second states that humour is always damaging because it always vents malice. McDougall (1963) argues further that it is the nature of the humour itself that distinguishes between that which can help or harm. McDougall defines 'high' humour as a form of therapeutic laughing which involves laughing with people rather than laughing at them. High humour is therapeutic because it creates a bond of friendship between those who share it. High humour does not wound because it is more than mere joke telling. It indicates a certain approach to life, work and oneself

---

5   Taken from Spiegl's '*A Small Book of Grave Humour.*'

in which fun is experienced by seeing the funny side to things without at the same time belittling others. Low humour on the other hand can be quite damaging because this usually involves laughing at people. Practical jokes, slapstick and jokes that attempt to draw attention to another person or group's perceived inferiority is what McDougall defines as low humour. However, given the situational nature of humour that often arises in life or death situations, it is difficult to categorise humour in this way. Because it is so contextual and frequently related to situations that are distasteful to begin with, gallows humour is often unavoidably of the type which McDougall might define as 'low' humour. But does this make it any less effective or helpful? A lot depends on who gets to hear it. It may be reasonable to say that as long as those who engage in 'gallows humour' show some discretion, then no real harm can come from it.

Release-related theories claim that laughter provides relief or mental, nervous and psychic energy and thus restores balance and calm after struggle, tension or strain. The most famous theory of this type was the theory of 'Gallows Humour' developed by Freud. Freud linked both humour and death to the sexual drive. According to Freud there were two opposing unconscious drives related to death. The first drive draws on the motivation to avoid death and Freud called this 'Eros'. The second conflicting drive, Freud called Thanatos, the death wish or at least, a desire for 'non being.' Humour in relation to both sexuality and death provides a release mechanism for socially unacceptable ideas or behaviour. More contemporary psychologists who take this position consider that humour forms part of an arousal-safety mechanism. Within this framework, laughter occurs when someone experiences heightened arousal but then evaluates the situation as safe or inconsequential.

In recent years there has been increasing evidence from the biological sciences to support the view that both laughter and tears have health benefits. Evidence that has accumulated over the years suggests that pent up stress can lead to a variety of health problems, including heart diseases, migraine, arthritis, diabetes and ulcerative colitis. Laughter and tears cause biological changes which discharge tension (Dugan, 1989). The tears and nasal secretions released when people experience humour, contain hormones, steroids and toxins that accumulate in the body during a stressful situation (Mazier, 1982).

When we laugh, the smile muscles on our faces contract. This stimulates certain glands[6] to release hormones that make the immune system work more effectively. This is important when we consider that people who are under a great deal of stress, tend to develop coughs and colds more easily. There is also some evidence to suggest that sexual differences in laughing and crying may also have a biological basis. Dugan writes that in almost all societies, women cry more than men and that this may be partly due to the secretion of a hormone called prolactin. Prolactin is instrumental in the production of both milk and other lachrymal secretions so that women may cry more because of higher prolactin levels. Such biological explanations offer much more than an interesting account for a difference in gender specific behaviour. Research also suggests that women may suffer less long-term ill effects from stressful situations than men because of their ability to openly express emotion. Cousens (1979) has argued that laughter can have analgesic properties. The reason for this has not yet been established but it may be that laughter encourages stimulation in the body of natural analgesics. Fry (1963) argues that laughter stimulates the circulatory system, exercises the lungs and also helps to reduce pain by distracting attention, reducing tension and increasing the production of endorphins.[7] Dugan cites Jonathan Swift's argument that 'the best doctors in the world are Dr Diet, Dr Quiet and Dr Merryman'. Laughter dissipates the biological imbalance caused by stressful situations. This suggests that humour can be very good for health (Simonton, 1978).

It has been suggested that humor in the workplace is often discouraged, although there is little evidence to support

6   The thymus gland that secretes thymosen. Thymosen is believed to make the immune system work more effectively.
7   Endorphins are natural substances produced by the body that help to control pain.

this claim. If true, it would be regrettable because humour is a source from which creative problem-solving can evolve (Abramis, 1992). This may be because humour provides a fresh perspective on the situations in which we find ourselves. Discouraging humour in the workplace may also perpetuate a climate in which psychosomatic and stress-related illnesses are more likely to occur (Hillman, 1994). The discouragement of humour in the workplace appears to be counterproductive. This is particularly so in a health care context where a condition known as 'burnout' has caused considerable concern in recent years. Basically 'burnout' occurs when people have to deal with constantly stressful situations without sufficient respite. In other words, 'burnout' occurs when people become emotionally and physically exhausted. The condition appears to be quite serious, because in America there are professional 'burnout' therapists who provide individual and group therapies designed to 'cure' sufferers.

Jaffe and Scott (1984) identified three stages to the process of a person developing 'burnout,' namely, tedium, negativity and disgust. During the first phase the person begins to feel fatigue, boredom and frustration with the job. During the second phase, the sufferer becomes increasing critical of others and during the third stage the person withdraws, avoiding all social contact. The person may continue to work, even in the latter stages of the condition. But a person who has progressed to the final stages will do as little work as possible. Jaffe and Scott argue that laughter in the workplace may be an effective way to prevent 'burnout' occurring. Whether or not the professional hierarchies disapprove of laughter, it is clear that many health care professionals use it as an effective coping strategy. Interviews conducted with the team at a hospital mortuary confirmed this view and so does the work of many writers on the topic. Below is an extract from the transcript of the mortuary interviews:

Interviewer: I was very impressed with what you were saying about how you developed your counselling skills. I think that was very good but could you tell me, do you think it helps if you have a certain type of personality to deal with this kind of work?

Interviewee 1:   Yes, I think that you need to be quite a bubbly sort of a person. You need to be the type of person who can shut the door and say 'goodbye death, hello life' and go home and leave the job behind you. You need to be able to see the funny side of life, and I don't mean that you need to be able to snap out of something, because many of the things that we see you just can't walk away from just like that, and they do get to you. But seeing the funny side does help.

Interviewee 2:   yes you do, I mean someone once said that to me 'oh you have a wicked sense of humour' but you do need that, yes. Its a way of coping with what's actually going on. Basically what we are dealing with is man's inhumanity to his fellow man and its not very nice. So you use humour to cope with it. I mean, I spent seven years in Northern Ireland scraping bodies off the streets, well you have to find a way to cope and humour is the main part of it. And of course, some of the situations we see here, some of the situations in which the bodies come in can be quite humorous.

As the speaker cited above states, the situations in which many people die can be quite funny. The inscribers of English gravestones have capitalised on this kind of situation humour when they have prepared some epitaphs. Take for example, poor John Tyrwitt, who in 1828 'died in a fit through drinking port wine.' And then there was Donald Robertson who died in 1848. His epitaph describes him as a 'peaceful quiet and Christian man' whose death was caused by the 'stupidity of Lawrence Tuloch of Clotherton who sold him nitre instead of Epson's salts by which he was killed in the space of three hours after taking a dose of it.' [8]

The epitaph above is humorous but at the same time judgmental. Thus, gallows humours is something of a paradox. It is, obviously, amusing but can also have quite serious

8   Each of the epitaphs cited above are taken from Spiegl (1971).

undertones. Freud (1961) believed that 'gallows humour' reduces stress because it provides an outlet for painful feelings which people find very hard to resolve. Looking for humour in situations that involve death or serious illness may seem distasteful but there is a wealth of evidence to suggest that it is a very appropriate way to deal with stress. Quite apart from the biological explanations we have discussed so far, laughter provides us with a different perspective on the problems we encounter. It is a powerful tool that can help us handle situations, in which we feel powerless (Klein, 1989). Humour also breaks down barriers between people and can be invaluable in therapeutic treatments. Humour is a form of communications that, due to its 'light-hearted' nature, often softens difficult interactions. It can dispel feelings of anger, resentment and embarrassment. In a healthcare context, patients may use humour in order to give themselves the upper hand in embarrassing situations. Terminally ill patients may use humour to help with coming to terms with their own impending death. For example, Klein writes of an AIDS patient who often joked about his illness. This man's fortieth birthday party invitations read, 'Rick's fortieth annual birthday party. He lived through another year. Can you believe it?' Of course there are times when the patient's premonition of impending death can be inaccurate. In such cases, humour can help 'save face'. Klein also writes of an old woman who retired to her bed because she was convinced that she was dying. Two or three days after her retirement, death had failed to make his predicted visit. So the woman got up to eat breakfast, saying 'well no one wants to die of an empty stomach.'

The playfulness of humour provides a vehicle to help steer us through difficult situations in life (Hillman, 1994). However, Klein cautions against indiscriminate use of humour in a health setting, pointing out that what is funny to one person can be very offensive to another. So although humour can be a bonding tool, it can backfire and cause alienation. He recommends that health care workers should establish a rapport with the patient before entering into any humorous interaction. He also advises caring professionals to listen to patients in order to find out what they find amusing.

Sometimes patients use humour as an indirect way of drawing attention to matters that may be causing them anxiety. In such cases, listening to the patient's jokes can pave the way to more serious and practical discussion aimed at resolving these concerns.

Incongruity-related theories focus on the fact that in many jokes, two seemingly incompatible phenomena are brought together. This position is consistent with the ideas of Kant who defined humour as 'an affection arising from sudden transformation of a strained expectation into nothing'. For a joke to be successful, the audience needs to be led along a certain path of comprehension, and then switched abruptly to another path by the punch line. Incongruity-related theories help to explain much of the seemingly inappropriate humour that arises in life and death situations. Death, or indeed any stressful situation, increases our experience of arousal. If something unusual and unexpected happens in the context of a stressful situation, outbursts of laughter and hilarity can occur. Sometimes people can laugh in situations such as this, without even knowing or understanding what it is at which they are laughing. Such laughter is irrational and may cause offence to those outside the situation who witness or hear of it.

Of course, the most likely place to find evidence of gallows humour is on a tomb or on gravestones. Spiegl (1971) cites the Churchyard's Handbook that states that:

> *'The object of an epitaph is to identify the resting place of the mortal remains of a dead person. It should, therefore, record only such information as is reasonably necessary for that purpose.'*

Despite this rather objective definition, Spiegl writes that:

> *'The writers and engravers of English tombstone inscriptions often displayed a deliciously witty turn of phrase in places and situations where one would have expected nothing but solemnity.'*

Given that we have concluded this book with a chapter on humour, it seems appropriate to end with some examples of epitaphs taken from English gravestones. Some of these continue the theme of sexuality and death explored in *Chapter 4*. For example, a gravestone in Edinburgh reads:

> *Here Lies*
> *Poor Charlotte*
> *Who died no Harlot — But in her virginity*
> *At the age of nineteen*
> *In this vicinity*
> *Rare to be found*
> *or seen!*

Another gravestone in Cornwall reads:

> *Here lyeth*
> *Ye body of*
> *Martha Dias*
> *Always noisy but very pious*
> *Who lived to the age of 3 score and 10*
> *And gave to worms*
> *What she refused to men.*

Jokes about the sexuality of the deceased are not limited to what inscribers had to say about women. Frequently, men suffered the brunt of this kind of gallows humours as well. A grave stone in Surrey reads:

> *Brigham Young*
> *Born on this spot — 1801*
> *A man of much courage*
> *And superb Equipment!*

Sometimes gallows humour can poke fun at the living as well as the dead. The epitaph below, for example, makes fun of the bereaved husband:

> *Here lyeth Mary, the wife of John Ford*
> *We hope that her soul has gone to the Lord*
> *But if for Hell she has changed this life*
> *She had better be there than John Ford's wife.*

References and bibliography

Abramis D (1992) Humour in Health Organisations. *Human Resource Management*, **August**: 72–4

Actherberg J (1985) *Imagery in Healing*. Rider Publications, London

Actherberg J (1990) *Women as Healer: A Comprehensive Survey from Prehistoric Times to the Present Day*. Rider Publications, London

Adams S (1993) A gendered history of the social management of death and dying in Foleshill, Coventry during the interwar years. In: Clark D, ed. *The Sociology of Death*. Blackwell Science, Oxford

Ainsworth R (1995) *The Lancashire Witches*. Aurora Press, Bolton

Anderson ML (1992) Editorial. *Gender Society* **6**(2): 163–7

Andrews L (1977) *No Time for Romance*. Corgi, London

Anon (1985) To the ones left behind: my laugh meant no disrespect. *Am J Nurs* **85**(8): 986

Anthony S (1971) *The Discovery of Death in Childhood and After*. Penguin, Harmondsworth

Aries P (1974) *Western Attitudes Towards Death*. John Hopkins University Press, London,

Aronson S (1992) Women's sense of responsibility for the care of old people: But who else will do it? *Gender Society* **6**(1): 8–29

Athlone Report, The (1939) Ministry of Health: Board of Education, London

Baldwinson D (1996) Reading War. Unpublished paper. Presented to The Health Sciences, Health Research Interest Group, South Bank University

Becker HS (1967) Whose side are we on? *Soc Prob* **14**: 239–47

Benner P (1989) *The Primacy of Care: Stress and Coping in Health and Illness*. Addison-Wesley Publishing, Menlo Park, CA

Bennett W (1957) *The Pendle Witches*. Lancashire County Books, Preston

Blanche HT, Parkes M (1997) *Christianity*. In: Parkes M,
    Laungani P, Young B, eds. Death and Bereavement Across
    Cultures. Routledge, London

Bonet J (1994) Is oral history autobiography? In: *Lives and Works:
    Autobiographic Occasions* 3: 1 and 3. University of
    Southampton, Southampton: 17–30

Bowlby J (1980) *Attachment and Loss*: Vol 3: Loss, Sadness and
    Depression. Hogarth Press, London

Bowling A, Cartwright A (1995) Caring for the spouse who died.
    In: Davis B, Gray A, Seale C, eds. *Health and Disease: A
    Reader*. Open University, Milton Keynes

Brendann E (1930) *Death Customs: An Analytical Study of Burial
    Rites*. Omnigraphics, Detroit

Brittain V (1933) *Testament of Youth: An Autobiographic Study of
    the Years 1900–1925*. Fontana, Glasgow

Burns N, Grove S (1987) *The Practice of Nursing Research,
    Critique and Utilisation*, WB Saunders, London

Cannandine D (1981) War and death: Grief and mourning in
    modern Britain. In: Whalley J, ed. *Mirrors of Mortality:
    Studies in the Social History of Death*. Bedford Square Press,
    London

Cant B (1997) *Invented Identities — Lesbians and Gays Talk About
    Migration*. Cassell, London

Clark S (1992) Action and reflection: Practice and theory in
    nursing. *J Adv Nurs* **13**(3): 295–8

Coakley BF (1992) *Improving the Academic Achievement of Third
    and Fourth Grade Underachievers as a Result of Improved
    Self-Esteem*. Heldref Publishing, Washington

Coles R (1989) *The Call of Stories*. Houghton Mifflin, Maryland

Conway J (1996) *Nursing Expertise and Advanced Practice*. Quay
    Books, Dinton

Conway MA (1990a) *Autobiographic Memory: An Introduction*.
    Open University Press, Milton Keynes

Coolican MB (1994) Families facing the sudden death of a loved
    one. Critical Care Hartford Hospital. *Nurs Clin N Am* **6**(3):
    607–12

Cousens N (1979) *The Anatomy of an Illness*. Norton, New York

Dale PN (1985) *Many Mansions: The Growth of Religion in Bolton:
    1750–1850*. Kwickprint, Bolton

Dalley G (1988) *Ideologies of Care: Rethinking Community Care and Collectivism*. Macmillan Press, Edinburgh

Davis JG (1988) Christianity. In Zaehner RC, ed. *Encyclopaedia of Living Faiths*. Century Hutchinson London

De Bois EC, Ruiz VI (1990) *Unequal Sisters*. Routledge, London

Dhalberg K (1994) Theory and caring practice as a collision of feminine and masculine cognitive style. *J Holist Nurs* 12(4): 83–99

Diamond J (1979) *Your Body Doesn't Lie*. Warner, New York

Dixon D (1989) The two faces of death: Children's magazines and their treatment of death in the Nineteenth century. In: Houlbrooke R, ed. *Death, Ritual and Bereavement*. Routledge, London

Doyle L, Rowbottam S, Scott A (1973) *Introduction to Witches, Midwives and Nurses*. Readers and Writers Publishing Cooperative, London

Dugan PO (1989) Laughter and tears: Best medicine for stress. *Nurs Forum* 24(1): 18–26

Ehrenriech B, English D (1973) *Witches, Midwives and Healers*. Readers and Writers Publishing Co-operative, London

Field D (1995) We didn't want him to die on his own — nurses accounts of dying patients. In: Davis B, Gray A, Seale C, eds. *Health and Disease: A Reader*. Open University Press, Milton Keynes

Fielding S (1994) *Murderous Bolton*. Owl Books, Wigan

Fielding S (1995) *The Hangman's Record, Vol 1. 1868–1899*. Chancery House Press, Kent

Finch J (1993) Its great to have someone to talk to: The ethics and politics of interviewing women. In: Hammersly M, ed. *Social Research: Philosophy, Politics and Practice*. Sage, London

Finch J, Groves D (1981) Community care and the family: A case for equal opportunities. *J Soc Policy* 9: 487–511

Finch J, Groves D, eds (1983) *A Labour of Love: Women, Work and Caring*. Routledge and Kegan Paul, London

Freud S (1961) Jokes and their relation to the unconscious. In: Strockey S, ed. *The Complete Psychological Works of Sigmound Freud*: Vol 8. Hogarth Press, London

Freud S (1973) Symbolism. In: Freud S. *Introductory Lecturers on Psychoanalysis*. Penguin, Harmondsworth

Frisby CL, Tucker CM (1993) Black children's perception of self: Implications for educators. *Educ Forum* **57**: 146–56

Frisch M (1990) *Shared Authority: Essays on the Craft and Meaning of Oral and Public History*. Aldany Suni Series, State University of New York, New York

Fry WF (1963) *Sweet Madness: A Study of Humour*. Pacific Books, Palo Alto

Fulton R (1995) The contemporary funeral: Functional or dysfunctional. In: Wass H, Niemeyer RA, eds. *Dying: Facing the Facts*. Taylor and Frances, London

Galtung J (1996) *Peace by Peaceful Means: Peace and Conflict, Development and Civilisation*. Sage, London

Geertz C (1957) Ritual and social change: A Japanese example. *Am Anthropol* **59**: 32–52

Gent L (1995) *Bolton Past*. Philimore and Co, Chichester

Glasier BG, Strauss AL (1967) *The Discovery of Grounded Theory: Strategies for Qualitative Research*. Aldine Press, Chicago

Gliner A (1986) *The Humour Approach to Humour on the Job*. The Humour Communication Co, Maryland MD

Goodman P (1994) Histories of the 2nd World War. unpublished paper. Manchester University, Manchester

Gorer G (1965) *Death, Grieving and Mourning in Contemporary Britain*. Cesset, London

Gough N (1989) From epistemology to ecopolitics: renewing a paradigm for curriculum. *J Curricul Stud* **21**(3): 243–53

Graham H (1993) Caring: A labour of love. In: Finch J, Groves D, eds. *A Labour of Love: Women, Work and Caring*. Routledge and Kegan Paul, London

Graham L (1993) Caring: A labour of love. In: Ungerson C, ed. *Gender and Caring: Work and Welfare in Britain and Scandinavia*. Routledge and Kegan Paul, London

Griffitts R (1988) *Agenda for Action*. HMSO, London

Hadenstien RW, Lamer WM (1963) *Funeral Customs the World Over*. Bufin Printers, Milwaukee

Haggis J (1990) The feminist process. In: Stanley L, ed. *Feminist Praxis*. Routledge, London

Hasted RA (1993) *The Pendle Witch Trial*. Lancashire County Books, Preston

Hibbert C (1977) *The Illustrated London News: Social History of Victorian Britain*. Morrison and Gibb, London and Edinburgh

Hillman S (1994) The healing power of humour at work. *Nurs Stand* **8**: 31–4

Hockey J (1985) Cultural and social interpretations of 'dying' and 'death' in a residential home for elderly people in the north east of London. *Curare* **8**(1): 35–43

Houlbrooke R (1989) Death, Ritual and Bereavement. Routledge, London

Hutchinson SA, Wilson HS, Wilson HS (1994) The benefits of participating in research interviews. *J Nurs Scholarship* **26**(2): 161–4

Illich I (1977) *Limitations to Medicine: Medical Nemesis and the Exploration of Health*. Penguin, Harmondsworth

Jacobi J (1968) *The Psychology of C G Jung*. Routledge and Kegan Paul, London

Jaffe D, Scott C (1984) *From Burnout to Practice*. McGraw-Hill, New York

Jarvis R (1907) *Chronicles of a Victorian Detective*. P D Riley, Cheshire

John AV (1992) *Scratching the Surface: Women, Work and Coal Mining History in England and Wales: Oral History*. Oral History Society, London

Johns C (1993) *Assessment of Practice: Ten Key Characteristics: The Challenge of Reflective Practice*. English National Board, London

Johnson E (undated paper) *Saving and Spending: The Working Class Economy in Britain 1870–1939*. Bolton Central Library, Local History Section, Bolton, Lancashire

Johnson K (1996) *Chilling True Tales of Old Lancashire*. Sigma Leisure, Cheshire

Jonker G (1997) The many facets of Islam: Death, dying and disposal between orthodox rule and historical convention. In: Parkes CM *et al*, eds. *Death and Bereavement Across Cultures*. Routledge London

Jung CG (1982) *Aspects of the Feminine*. Ark Paperbacks, London and New York

Kalish RA (1985) *Death, Grief and the Caring Relationship*, 2nd edn. Brooks Cole, California

Kastenbaum RJ (1972) Is Death a life crisis? On the confrontation with death in theory and practice. In: Datan M, Ginsberg LH, eds. *Life Span Developmental Psychology: Normative Life Crisis*. Academic Press, New York

Kastenbaum R (1988) Safe death in the post modern world. In: Gilmore A, Gilmore S, eds. *A Safer Death: Multidisciplinary Aspects of Terminal Care*. Plenum Press, London

Kearl MC (1995) Death and politics: A psychosocial perspective. In: Wass H, Neimeyer RA, eds. *Dying: Facing the Facts*, 3rd edn. Taylor and Frances, USA

Kelly SL (1988) The Disposal of the Dead in nineteenth century Bolton Research. Presented for MA Manchester University, Bolton Central Library, Local Studies Section

Kenny C (1992) Echoes Unpublished MSc Thesis undertaken as part completion for the MSc Practitioner Research, Manchester Metropolitan University, Department of Health care Studies, Elizabeth Gaskell, Hathersage Road, Manchester

Kenny C (1993 and in press) *Foucault, Power/Knowledge and the Case of the EN*. Paper presented at the Nursing, Women's History and the Politics of Welfare Conference, Nottingham University, Nottingham (to be published by Nottingham University Press)

Kenny C (1994) *Cotton Everywhere: Recollections of Northern Women Mill Workers*. Aurora, Bolton

Kenny C, Wibberley C (1994) The case for interactive interviewing. *Nurse Researcher* 1(3): 57–64

Kfir N, Slevin M (1991) *Challenging Cancer: From Chaos to Control*. Tavistock/Routledge, London

Klein A (1989) The lighter side of death: Listening for laugher. *J Nurs Jocul* 4(1): 10–11

Kubler Ross E (1969) *On Death and Dying*. Macmillan, New York

Langan M (1992) Who cares: Women in the fixed economy of care. In: Langan M, Day L, eds. *Women, Oppression and Social Work: Issues in Anti Discriminatory Practice*. Routledge, London

Laungani P (1995) Patterns of bereavement in Indian and British Society. *Bereavement Care Newsletter*, South Bank University Division of Psychology

Laungani P (1997) Death in a Hindu family. In: Parkes CM, Laungani P, Young B, eds. *Death and Bereavement Across Cultures*. Routledge, London

Leaney J (1989) Ashes to ashes: Cremation and the celebration of death in nineteenth century Britain. In: Houlbrooke R, ed. *Death, Ritual and Bereavement*. Routledge, London

Levine E (1997) Jewish views and customs on death. In: Parkes CM *et al*, eds. *Death and Bereavement Across Cultures*. Routledge, London

Litten J (1991) *The English Way of Death: The Common Funeral Since 1450*. Robert Hale Limited, London

Littewood J (1992) *Aspects of Grief: Studies of Bereavement in Adult Life*. Routledge, London

Lumby J (1995) *The Lancashire Witch Craze: Janet Preston and the Lancashire Witches*. Carnegie Publishing Limited, Preston

Lummis T (1987) *Listening to History*. Barnes and Noble Books, London

Lynch J (1960) *The Broken Heart: The Medical Consequences of Loneliness*. McGraw Hill, New York

Mackay GE (1980) Premature burials. *Popular Sci Mthly* **16**: 389–97

Mazier E (1982) 10 sure fire stress releasers. *Prevention* **34**: 104–6

McDougall W (1963) *An Instinct of Laughter: An Introduction to Social Psychology*. Union Paperbacks, New York

McKeon R (1977) Person and community: metaphysical and political. *Ethics* **88**: 207–17

Meller P (1993) Death in high modernity: The contemporary absence and presence of death. In: Clark D, ed. *The Sociology of Death*, Blackwell, Oxford

Miles M (1993) Towards a methodology for feminist research. In: Hammersley M, ed. *Social Research: Philosophy, Politics and Practice*. Sage, London

Morley J (1971) *Death, Heaven and the Victorians*. Routledge, London

Moyle W, Bernard A, Charne T (1995) The humanities and nursing: Using popular literature as a means of understanding human experience. *J Adv Nurs* **21**: 960–4

Mulkey M (1993) Social death in Britain. In: Clark D, ed. *The Sociology of Death*. Blackwell Science, Oxford

Nettleton S (1995) *The Sociology of Health and Illness*. Polity Press, Cornwall

Nicholas G (1904) *A History of the English Poor Law*: Vol 2. Orchard House, Westminster

Oakley A (1979) Wise women and medicine men: Changes in the management of childbirth. In: Mitchell J, Oakley A, eds. *The Rights and Wrongs of Women*. Penguin Books, Harmondsworth

Oakley A (1991) Interviewing women: A contradiction in terms. In: Roberts H, ed. *Doing Feminist Research*. Routledge, Kegan Paul, London

Oliver M (1992) Changing the social relations of research production. *Disabil Handicap Society* **7**(2): 101–14

Palmer C (1993) Theory without jargon. *Trouble Strife* **26**: 2

Parker D (1944) Local history: How to gather it, write it, and publish it. In: Josephson BE. ed. *Doing Local History*. Social Science Research Council, New York

Parker I (1991) *Discourse Dynamics*. Sage, London

Parkes CM (1972) *Bereavement: Studies of Grief in Adult Life*. Routledge, London

Parkes CM, Laungani P, Young B (1997) *Death and Bereavement Across Cultures*. Routledge, London

Payne S (1991) Why are women poor? In: Payne S, ed. *Women, Health and Poverty*. Harvester Wheatsheaf, Hemel Hempstead

Pojman LP (1992) *Life and Death; Grappling with the Moral Dilemmas of Our Time*. Jones & Bartlett Publishing, London

Purkiss D (1996) *The Witch in History: Early Modern and Twentieth Century Representations*. Routledge, London

Raphael B (1984) *The Anatomy of Bereavement: A Handbook for the Caring Professional*. Hutchinson, London

Raskin (1985) Psychological theories of humour. *Psychol Today* **October**: 34–9

Ratna L, Davis P (1984) Family therapy with the elderly: Some strategies and techniques. *Br J Psychol* **145**(3): 311–15

Richardson R (1988) The nest egg and the funeral: Fear of death in the parish amongst the elderly. In: Gilmore A, Gilmore S, eds. *Towards a Safer Death: Multi Disciplinary Aspects of Terminal Care*. Plenum Press, New York

Richmond BJ, Rose MW (1994) Responses to AIDs-related bereavement. *J Psychosoc Ontol* **2**(1/2): 143–63

Roberts E (1989) The Lancashire way of death. In: Houlbrooke R, ed. *Death, Ritual and Bereavement*. Routledge, London

Rose P, Parker DC (1994) Nursing: an integration of art and sciences within the experience of the practitioner. *J Adv Nurs* **20**: 1004–10

Rosenblatt PC (1997) Grief in small scale societies. In: Parkes M *et al*, eds. *Death and Bereavement Across Cultures*. Routledge, London

Rycroft C (1979) *The Innocence of Dreams: A New Approach to the Study of Dreams*. Pantheon Books, London

Scarre G (1987) *Witchcraft and Magic in Sixteenth and Seventeenth Century Europe*. Macmillan, London

Scott A (1584) *The Discovery of Witchcraft*. Centaur Press, New York

Schoeder-Skeker T (1994) Music of the dying: A personal account of the new field of music — thanatology — history, theory and clinical narratives. *J Holistic Nurs* **12**(1): 83–99

Scull A (1996) Asylums: Utopias and realities. In: Carter J, Thomlinson D, eds. *Asylum in the Community*. Routledge, London

Sieber JE (1992) *Planning Ethically Responsible Research: A Guide for Students and International Review Boards*. Sage, London

Simonton C (1978) *Getting Well Again*. Union Paperbacks, New York

Skidmore D (1995) *The Ideology of Community Care*. Chapman and Hall, London

Small S (1985) Deathwork: A Sociological Analysis of Funeral Directing. Unpublished PhD Thesis, University of Surrey

Sontag S (1993) Illness as metaphor. In: Basiro D, Gray A, Seale C eds. *Health and Disease: A Reader*, 2nd edn. Open University Press, Milton Keynes

Spender H (1995) *Worktown People: Photographs from Northern England: 1937–38*. Mulford J, ed. Falling House Press, Bristol

Spiegl F (1971) *A Small Book of Grave Humour*. Pan Books, London

Stanley L (1994) Thoughts on cotton everywhere. In: Kenny C, ed. *Cotton Everywhere: Recollections of Northern Women Mill Workers*. Aurora Publishing, Bolton

Starhawk (1979) Spiral dance. In: Brooke E, ed. *A Woman's Book of Shadows: Witchcraft: A Celebration*. Women's Press, London

Stuart M (1993) And how was it for you Mary? Self identity and meaning for oral historians. *J Oral History Society* **21**(2): 20–30

Summers M (1995) *Witchcraft and Black Magic*. Senate, London

Taylor L (1983) *Mourning Dress: A Costume and Social History*. Allen and Unwin, London

Thomas K (1971) *Religion and the Decline of Magic*. Penguin, Harmondsworth

Thompson P (1978) *The Voice of History*. Open University Press, Milton Keynes

Trevor-Roper HR (1969) *The European Witch Craze of the Sixteenth and Seventeenth Centuries*. Penguin, London

Twigg C (1984) *The Black Death: A Biological Appraisal*. Batsford, London

Ungerson C (1984) The politics of community care. In: Ungerson C ed. *Gender and Care: Work and Welfare in Britain and Scandinavia*. Harvester Wheatsheaf, Hertfordshire

Ussher J (1991) *Women's Madness: Misogyny and Mental Illness*. Harvester Wheatsheaf, Hertfordshire

Usserwood B (1992) Community information. In: Kendell M, ed. *Informing Communities*. Newcastle, Community Services Group for the Library Association, Newcastle on Tyne: 19–39

Waerness K (1990) Informal and formal care in old age. In: Ungerson C, ed. *Gender and Caring: Work and Welfare in Britain and Scandinavia*. Harvester Wheatsheaf, Hertfordshire

Wainwright S (1994) Analysing data using grounded theory. In: *Nurse Researcher,* Vol 1, no 3. Scutari Press, Harrow

Walter T (1997) Secularisation. In: Parkes M, *et al*, eds. *Death and Bereavement Across Cultures*. Routledge , London

Warren RL (1955) *Studying Your Community*. Collier-Macmillan Limited, London

References

Webb C (1986) *Feminist Practice in Women's Health Care.* John Wiley & Sons, Chichester

Wilson A, Levey H (1938) *Burial Reform and Burial Costs.* Oxford University Press, Oxford

Yorder L (1994) Comfort and consolation: A nurse's perspective on parental bereavement. *Pediatr Nurs Women Children Serv* **29**(5): 473–7

Young G (1981) Hospice and health care. In: Sauders C, Summers DH, Teller N, eds. *Hospice: The Living Idea.* Edward Arnold, London

Young M, Cullen L (1996) *A Good Death: Conversations with East Londoners.* Routledge, London

Zernou (1988) Christianity: The Eastern Schism and the Eastern Orthodox Church. In: Zaehner RC, ed. *The Encyclopaedia of Living Faiths.* century Hutchinson, London

Ziegler P (1969) *The Black Death.* Penguin, London

Index